D1633554

All in a Day's Work
Stories by The Country Matchmaker

Patricia Warren

Illustrated by Nik

First published 2003

Copyright © Patricia Warren

Many of the stories in 'All in a Day's Work' are loosely based on actual accounts and I have taken the liberty of embellishing some of the tales and changed identities and locations of some of the characters in order to maintain client confidentiality.

All rights reserved. No parts of this publication, including text or illustrations, may be reproduced or stored in a retrieval system, or transmitted, in any form or by any means, electronic, mechanical, photocopying, recording or otherwise without prior permission of the publisher, Farming Books and Videos Ltd.

ISBN 0-9542555-9-3

A catalogue record for this book is available from the British Library

Published by
Farming Books and Videos Ltd.
PO Box 536, Preston PR2 9ZY
United Kingdom

www.farmingbooksandvideos.com

Illustration, design and layout
Nikki Moore, Pigsty Studio
www.pigstystudio.co.uk

Printed and bound in Great Britain by Butler & Tanner, Frome

Acknowledgements

I wish to thank David Adams and Kathryn from Wales who continually badgered me to write this book. Jill Tait for her constant help, constructive criticism and encouragement. Rosina Newton and John Rollason for proof reading and John, my husband. He has mentioned how he's a saint for putting up with me - he probably is.

Of course, without the hundreds of Bureau clients who have let me be part their lives this book would not have been written. They have given me their friendships and allowed me to record their exciting, happy, sad and lonely moments. I sincerely thank them all.

Foreword

As Chair of the Association of British Introduction Agencies I feel it is a privilege and an honour to have been asked to write the foreword to Patricia's first book.

Patricia set up 'The Farmers and Country Bureau' over twenty years ago with the sole aim of helping rural dwellers find love and to make a living through doing something she enjoyed: Matchmaking!

This book, like the author, exudes warmth and integrity. The characters and emotions are vividly painted and their stories lovingly told and intertwined with great humour.

She shows throughout her book the care and attention that each client merits and she never loses sight of the trust placed in her by the individuals she sets out to help. Its main subject, matchmaking, is one of the world's oldest professions and requires dedication, insight and, above all, empathy. The stories show a wealth of these qualities.

Patricia also describes life on her upland livestock farm, situated in the picturesque Peak District of Derbyshire, with accounts of the typical working day of a farmer's wife and all the tasks and tribulations this entails. If your interest is just in the country, even if you are an urban or city dweller, you will be intrigued by the descriptions of farm life.

I recommend this book to all who have a genuine interest in the countryside and the rich characters who inhabit it. 'All in a Day's Work' gives an account of modern country life told with great sympathy and amusement.

Well done Patricia. A thoroughly enjoyable read.

Lynda Davies
Chair of the Association of British Introduction Agencies.

Chapters

Chapter

1.
Make Hay While the Sun Shines

I was leisurely crossing the farmyard to my office one peaceful summer morning. It was very early and as I gazed across the fields the mist was still in the valley with the promise of a hot sunny day ahead. Suddenly the phone started ringing. I quickened my steps and rushed to snatch up the receiver, preparing myself for the usual polite, "Good morning, Patricia Warren speaking, The Farmers and Country Bureau." But the caller didn't give me a chance. He just waded straight in. "George 'ere. That lass you fixed me up wi. 'She's no bloody good. Too tight wi' 'er money."

Well, I wasn't too fazed, but this was very plain speaking indeed for six o'clock in the morning. It was obvious that he was a Yorkshireman, and after a few seconds my brain clicked into gear and I remembered who he was.

"Oh it's you George. Well I'm sorry to hear things aren't working out with you and Joan. You've been going out for quite a while haven't you? I take it then that you won't want to see her again. But you know, you really should tell her that yourself if you feel you can."

"Now Mrs. Warren," he continued and I could tell I was in for some Yorkshire reasoning here, "I didna say that I want to stop seein' 'er - not just yet like. An' I'll tell thee for why. What it is, she's knittin' me a jumper - 'er an' me mother between 'em. She's doin' the body and me mother's knittin' the sleeves. So I canna finish wi' 'er till it's all joined up, else it'll be a waste o' good wool. But I dunna want 'er for a wife, 'cus 'er is too tight wi er money, an' dunna thee worry, I shall tell 'er so when t'jumper's finished."

My mouth dropped open at his words and I had to quickly bring the conversation to an end and put the phone down before I exploded with laughter. Well, I've come across every kind of man that God has made and all the forms of human courtship that there can be in the universe, from the suave and sophisticated to blunderings beyond belief, but this was truly the limit.

You know, a lot of people do treat introduction agencies with a sort of scornful humour, giving a laugh here and a joke there when the subject comes up, and this story about George is absolutely true. But often humour just covers up an inability to take control of our own lives and do something positive about meeting someone special. I suppose you have to get a balance and treat joining a bureau quite light- heartedly. After all life is fun and meeting others should be enjoyable and relaxed. But also treat it with the sincerity and the significance that it deserves because if it works it can change the whole of someone's life.

I've been passionate about matchmaking all my life, from the days when I used to match my dolls, and I'm pleased to say it has brought me immense satisfaction. I feel that helping others to meet a life partner is a very worthy service to be providing. I treat it seriously and I try to provide this service to the very highest standards. In this respect I will not compromise and would never allow anyone to join who I thought for one moment would not treat other members respectfully and well. That's quite heavy stuff, you might say. Well yes, but I am dabbling with people lives, wishes, desires, hopes and expectations and to do my very best by a strict moral code has always been vitally important to me.

I couldn't settle down to work in the Bureau that morning. George had made me laugh so much with his contradictions. My mind started to wonder over the incredible differences that occur in human nature. How amazing it is that men and women ever get together and stay together at all.

But before I had time to continue with my thoughts that morning I had a phone call from Megan, a client in Wales. Her voice was kind and soft, thoughtful, worldly and beautifully lilting with a deep Welsh accent. She had been going out for nearly a year with David, a farmer from North West Wales. She began her conversation by saying she thought I would be in my office early on such a lovely summer's day and then continued by telling me that she loved David very much and believed that he also loved her, but they had seemed to run into difficulties. Could she talk this through with me and ask for a bit of advice?

"I love him dearly but so often he just doesn't want to talk to me. I want him so much to tell me his feelings and be a bit romantic, but it's as if any show of emotion is taboo and he will not let it come to the surface."

"Well, I know what you mean Megan," I replied. "Men are a breed apart, particularly some who throughout their childhood would not have been encouraged by their parents to talk openly. David's very much like my husband."

"Your husband!" Megan echoed, "I wouldn't have thought you would have chosen a man who couldn't show his feelings easily."

"Well I did." I replied "John's so bad at speaking in an emotional way that a few weeks ago, when he knew he really ought to try, it turned into a complete disaster."

I told her about what had happened at my father's funeral. I stood at the graveside, weeping and generally very sad while John tried desperately to cheer me up. Looking down, he turned and toed with his shoe the fresh deep brown earth newly dug out around the grave. "Never mind love," he murmured, "He's in a good place here, just look at the quality of the soil. It's really good stuff."

I told Megan that as I looked up at him standing by my side at the grave I was completely appalled and dumbfounded by his attempt to be comforting. Then I just had to see the funny side of it. He had tried so hard to be reassuring but his inept use of words at this extremely emotional moment had seemed so awful.

Megan laughed with me and said it did seem that men find it hard to talk about feelings. She went on to describe how she and David had drifted apart and all she wanted was to regain the closeness they once had. At David's farm his son, who had recently joined his father, was constantly on the scene and this was rather disconcerting, although generally he was a lovely boy and she was very fond of him. I said to Megan it sounded as if she and David needed to find some time completely alone and they should try to meet up somewhere one day a week, away from the farm, somewhere central between her home and David's. She said Betwsy-Coed would be a good place, and when I suggested they book into a hotel there for the odd afternoon indulgence, she said she thought I was being rather naughty. Sometimes, thinking outside the square can provide the right answer.

Rosie, my secretary at the time, was sitting in the office whilst I was taking the call and she seemed to have picked up on what I was talking about, "Oh yes, there are some lovely hotels around that area," she said. "I've visited most of them."

I replied that it wouldn't surprise me the way she'd been getting about recently. Rosie had applied for the job about a year previously and at the time she had been married for about twenty five years to a local farmer. I like to employ staff with a farming background as they have a better understanding of my clients. She was in her fifties, well built, with grey hair, and never wore makeup. She parted from her husband about six months into the job and she had changed from being a quiet un-noticed, non-descript woman to someone who was definitely enjoying life in all ways. Some mornings she would arrive in her car with great speed saying she never thought she'd make it on time. Then she would go on to explain that she had just driven from the other side of the county to make the nine am start. Every time she would tell me she'd met up with a new friend (male) the previous evening and that time had just 'flown by,' so she'd had to stay the night. With my naive and unexciting lifestyle, I would marvel and laugh at the things she would tell me about her recent romantic exploits.

Then one day I started to piece together remarks made to me by some of the middle aged gents on my register. They didn't want to have another introduction at the moment as they had been promised a date by a lady they had been speaking to recently. Rosie had been chatting up my clients and promising to meet up with them! On questioning her, she had not gone ahead with any of these encounters, but it had got pretty close. Sadly Rosie had to go as I could not have such conduct, but I missed her amusing stories. It also taught me not to typecast anyone. The most dowdy or colourless character can have unimaginable talents hiding beneath the surface just waiting to get out.

In the twenty years that the bureau has now been established I have of course employed a number of secretaries and got on well with them all. They usually stay for a long time and then the seven year itch afflicts them and they are beckoned by pastures new. My secretaries have been friends, baby sitters, confidantes and companions, and very deep friendships have been cemented between us. None, however, would ever take on the task of doing the real 'dirty work' when it came to speaking plainly to difficult clients. Marjorie, a local farmer, worked part time for me. She did the farming alongside her husband and son. Being the most mature, she would occasionally help me out with being very frank with some clients on the telephone but when it came to doing the real nitty-gritty it was always left to me to handle the really awful situations.

One farmer came through the door smelling so bad that he outdid the muck cart which, from time to time, sweeps past on its way to the fields. I was fully expecting his arrival but when he came through the door, I could not believe the smell. It was not just an ordinary country smell either. I was pleasant and nice to him. I always try to put people at their ease. I asked what sort of farming he did, and when he said he reared pigs, I realised what the smell was. I took a deep breath to steady myself for some plain talking, and nearly passed out from the fumes. I asked if anything unusual had happened on the farm that day, thinking that maybe all the stock had got loose and he had not had time to shower or change his clothes, but he assured me everything was fine.

"Well please forgive me for bringing this up," I said, "But would you go out with a lady I introduced you to in those clothes. They do smell a bit of pigs."

Immediately his bristles came out and he was most indignant. He promptly told me that he would not stand for such insults and walked out of the office. When I had had time to recover, I reflected that this reaction would have been a cover for his embarrassment. What a shame. But I don't know how else I could have approached the subject.

On another occasion I had to talk to Charles, a well educated man in his early thirties. He was a graduate who had gone on to become an accountant and worked for a large company in the Midlands. He had been brought up on a small farm but he had been encouraged to 'go off and make something of his life.' He had no definite accent and he had told me previously that his parents had done years of hard work with little reward and they were determined that he would not be in the same position as them. 'Get yourself a proper job and become an accountant' they cried. Throughout his childhood he had followed their wishes but in his twenties and thirties he was totally frustrated because of the overriding fact that he loved farming and hated his accountancy work. The lure of the countryside was so intense that he had actually bought himself a small farm and worked it at the weekends. However, when he spoke to me, the thing that came to my attention, as it had done in previous conversations, was that as he spoke he continually swore and used bad language.

"The last bloody woman didn't work out. Just like the others they didn't even bloody well phone back. It's a bugger really."

I noticed from his file that he had received about five introductions, and none had gone any further than speaking on the telephone. It suddenly dawned on me that he must have been using bad language in the course of telephone conversations with women. How strange it was for him to be like this. In some ways you would be able to accept this language more easily from a brusque old farmer, rather than from this young professional. I realised I had to bring this swearing out in the open.

"I don't know if you realise it Charles but do you know that you swear quite a lot in your everyday conversation, even when you are on the telephone?"

All went quiet at this chastisement and I imagined his frown deepened.

"I do a bit, don't I," he replied in a subdued manner.

I told him if he spoke to his potential partners as he spoke to me, it certainly would not create a good impression.

"I want you to make a concerted effort that not one word of swearing will be uttered from your lips when you speak to the next girl."

"I'll certainly try Pat," he said, as meek and mild as a little lamb, obviously transported back to the days of a dragon of a schoolteacher laying down the rules and regulations.

"Well that went rather well," I said to myself and got back to my paperwork.

More common though is the man who wants everything. I answered the phone one day to a broad country accent, slightly Welsh but also incorporating the lovely rural voice of Shropshire. He introduced himself and said he was a farmer and he had never been married but he was looking for a wife.

"She's got to be a farmer's daughter working on her dad's farm. I don't want someone who goes out to work. She must never have been married. I don't really want her to have had boyfriends. Someone in her early thirties. I've thought about twenties, but I think that is a bit young for me."

"Let's talk about you first," I replied.

He went on to introduce himself as Ivor and told me that his father was very old and quite ill and that the woman he was looking for must be prepared to look after him. He then said, "Of course I want children." I took all this in and listened intently to his conversation and before too long little red warning lights started to appear in my mind.

"Tell me Ivor," I said, "Why does she have to be a farmer's daughter and working on her dad's farm?"

"In case I die," he immediately said.

"What do you mean?" I asked, visualising that this poor man knew he had a dreaded terminal illness.

"So that my son will have someone to look after the farm until he is old enough to take over."
"You have a son?" I asked.

"Not yet," he replied. "But she will give me a son and then that is my plan afterwards, in case I die."

"But what if you didn't have a son? What if all the children you had were daughters? Or what if you and a future wife didn't even have children?"

"Well, she'd be no good for me if she couldn't have any children, would she?"

"But what if you were the infertility factor in all this?" I asked, just in the hope of shocking him. It then suddenly dawned on me I had better find out his age. "Fifty six," came the reply.

"Gosh Ivor!" I said "There are not many ladies who approach me in their thirties who would consent to be introduced to a man in his fifties, you know. The other fact is that any woman would want to be wanted for herself. She would want to fall in love with you, and expect that your relationship would be the most special thing between you, not her ability to breed - and to only breed sons!"

The conversation that morning was not unique. Over the years I have had hundreds of men around that age and older approach the bureau to really only produce a son and heir. The oldest was eighty six!

That year seemed to be full of older men and the romance they wished to re-capture in the autumn of their lives. For later on that summer I had to tread very carefully in a highly diplomatic and sensitive task connected with my father and the ladies in his life.

My mother and father had married at the onset of war in 1939, when they were eighteen and twenty, having met and courted throughout their teenage years. They had a happy marriage for over forty years and never deviated from their love and devotion to each other. Sadly my mother died in her early sixties. Once by himself dad decided to be positive, and went out and enjoyed every moment of the next ten years.

When he died, as sole executor of his Will, I knew I had to read through the wording very precisely.

'Any three framed prints, of her personal choice, by Sir William Russell Flint, to be given to Nanette Calander and also my statue of a nude female person which stands thirty inches tall. I also bequeath fifteen thousand pounds to the said Nanette Calander to be enjoyed by her without hindrance.

'A print depicting a nude female lying on a bed to be given to Joah Riley.'

'A statuette of a nude female and male person entitled 'The Union,' to Sarah Kelly.'

'A nude male and female bronze entitled 'The Kiss,' to be given to Alice Johnson.'

So it went, on and on, with exact instructions for the disposal of gifts to different ladies.

I knew my journey down to the family home in Worcestershire to carry out his wishes would be sad but laced with a little humour. I had to receive each of the ladies that my father called his 'girlfriends' to his house and tell each of his bequests to them. The old devil had warned me before hand, with a mischievous twinkle in his eye, "You'll have to sort it out for me after I've gone".

First I saw dad's most 'special' lady, whom I knew he loved very much. Nanette and my father had been lovers for about nine years and, although they spent most of their weekdays apart, they joined up and had very sociable and exciting weekends. I knew he met up with the other ladies for occasional evenings and days out but none were in the same category as Nanette.
It worked rather well really with Nannette spending most of the morning with me at dad's house and then we had lunch together. I'd planned that in the afternoon each of the other ladies would arrive separately on the hour throughout the rest of the day.

I read the relevant paragraph in the Will to each them and accompanied them to the appropriate part of the house and the scene of the erotic objet d'art. They all depicted themselves as my favourite grandmother which seemed strange when handing over such explicit images and as they were not gift wrapped they were clearly visible to all passers by as they carried them out of the house.

Nanette went away with her bequests safely placed in the back of her car.

For the rest I'd received instructions from dad, in his Will that to each item that was given to the other ladies, I was to attach a small white card with the words:
'So you may contemplate on what never was - but could have been'.

The second lady read the card and cried a little then placed her bequest in a large carrier bag. The third, with 'The Union,' read the card and gave an almighty laugh and tucked the sculpture under her arm. Then the forth, just smiling at the quotation placed 'The Kiss' on the passenger seat next to her in her car.

"You wicked old man," I repeated again, as I talked to the walls around me, hoping my words might reverberate up to heaven or quite possibly down to hell to be heard by my old dad.

Knowing I was going to Worcestershire for a short while I accepted an invitation from two clients to visit them a little further south, in Gloucestershire. So the next day I journeyed down through Evesham then on to Cheltenham and drove around the outskirts of Gloucester. I stopped and had lunch with a veterinary friend and his wife who have a farm in Gloucestershire, then continued on my way descending slowly from a high escarpment into the valley below. As I drove down I could see a wonderful view of the county for miles ahead. It was slightly dimmed by the heat haze across the horizon, but it was a most beautiful hot summer afternoon. Fields spread for miles in front of me dotted with the comings and goings of farming activity. The scene unfolded before me and I felt as if I could touch every individual field. It looked like an immense, brilliantly coloured, patchwork quilt.

Tractors and trailers were trundling to and fro. Men, some closer but others tiny in the distance, were enthusiastically jumping on and off machinery, walking around fields or directing other people. This was going on virtually everywhere. It reminded me of scenes from Toy Town in my old Noddy books.

I weaved my way through the narrow high-hedged lanes. It was a bit of a lottery really as you could not see for more than a few yards ahead with blind corners constantly in your way. My driving was, of course, dead slow and as I entered the lower land of the valley the pungent, warm, musky smell of hay hit me. The smell was so overpowering and so lovely that I stopped the car. I took in huge breaths of such a nostalgic smell. Tractors started trying to pass me but it was impossible so in a handy gate close by I pulled up and turned off the engine.
I got out of the car and surveyed the close fields. Yes, people and tractors were scurrying around and the glorious smell of hay intoxicated me. The smell made me think about the farm back home in Derbyshire and with having to stop for a while I remembered back to our days of haymaking.

We haven't made hay for over twenty years and John will say that those who say 'What a pity' were never the people who actually worked every moment of the day and night to make it. "Bloody hard work," he would say. "It's hot, sweaty and dirty and if you've got to make up to twenty thousand bales you will work harder than you have ever done in your life."

As the farmer's wife I remember being on a knife's edge in the early mornings. 'Will the weather be good enough for him to start mowing?' You had to judge it just right so that you could mow and ted and row it all in succession to produce those much wanted final bales. The stress accumulated dramatically in the early mornings and we all waited for my husband, John, to make the decision, 'Will he, won't he?' We all wanted to get going but he knew that with the wrong decision the worst hay in the world would be made. I would want him to get going for my own insignificant and selfish reason; so that my cakes and pies that I had made over the previous days for the men wouldn't go stale.

"We're going!" I would hear him say and we all knew then that everything for those following days would be centred on getting the hay. It was a frenzied rush. You dreaded a breakdown, no matter how hard you had prepared and serviced the machinery in the previous weeks. It always happened. I, like all other wives, would be on call to get new parts instantly, to take the curses and to keep quiet no matter what he said to you. In my first year of marriage I was so upset when John started shouting at me after the machinery broke down and I'd done nothing to cause it. I complained to my mother on the phone. "He has to blame the injustices of a breakdown on someone and it can't be the men so it has to be you. Your dad was just like that. Now keep quiet, keep out of the way and just pray that all will get going again soon." The tension and stress at those difficult times would seem insurmountable. Then, with the sun and success as the hay was bailed, the relief would start to slowly creep in.

It was always my job to fetch the men in the late afternoon and early evening to help with the carting. We would never leave a bale outside overnight in case it rained. Because we used to make such a lot we needed much help in those summer evenings and about twelve good men and true would come from the village of Youlgrave about two miles away.

I would go out and help load and John was always in the barn stacking. We all knew our jobs and it was usually done with great humour. You made sure you kept the working men in a good mood as their help at this time was so crucial. Cider and beer went around in abundance throughout the evening. It did not matter really how much the men drank as long as it kept their thirst at bay and they kept working. After two or three hours work I would go and take their tea out to the fields. There was much bantering and jokes. That half hour would be a good time and refreshed everyone so they worked even harder afterwards.

By the time it was dark and all the hay for that day was in and stacked the men would come to the house for meat and pickles and more drink. John would collapse into bed. I would be washing up and thinking about what food needed to be prepared for the next day,

With a good crop and the very last bale safely in the feelings of relief were immense and these feelings would not subside until after the next day when we would have our supper at a local pub. All the men would come along but this time well dressed and ready for a good time. We would provide a large meal and drink would be flowing. Goodbyes to the once a year casual men would be said and when we got home I knew that John would have the best and most deserved sleep of the year.

Then I remembered what I was supposed to be doing that afternoon. I was visiting David and Katie. I manoeuvred my car back onto the narrow lane and continued to negotiate rural Gloucestershire.

Driving towards David and Katie that afternoon I wondered about this couple, as I always do, when I am asked to come and visit. I remembered David as being in his early thirties. He was a farmer's son who worked as a blacksmith. As sincere and nice a person as you would ever wish to meet. When he first joined the Bureau he had had quite a hard knock with one particular previous romance and so was quite disillusioned and disheartened. He was tallish and broad with fair hair and a great smile.

After arriving at their neat, small house, with a refreshing long drink in my hand, I sat down and glanced around at this young couple's home. It was a cottage style house that was small and cosy but had the advantages of being very new. Inside was bright, cheerful and stylish and all the walls were a mellow yellow.

David had been realistic in his search for a partner. He knew he had got to meet more people to find that one special person but meeting her through an introduction agency was not how he thought he was going to do it. As we talked he described how his choice was to find a nice rural pub which a country girl might use as her local. He decided that The Beacon Hotel at Haresfield, just three miles away, was the place where he might stand a chance, and he went there, particularly on the nights when they had live music. But no matter how much he tried, he met no one. In the end he realised he needed another way of meeting someone and that was when he decided to join the Bureau.

Katie was his first introduction and he was the first person she met with the Bureau. She was in her early thirties, single and a farmer's daughter who worked as a nursery nurse. She was blond with a warm, round and friendly face and nature. She had had boyfriends and one in particular had been serious before, but just like David, she had been hurt.

David was amazed when he got her profile. She actually lived quite close to where The Beacon Hotel was. He was astounded at this and thought it could not be true. Maybe someone was playing a practical joke on him.

As he was talking Katie butted into the conversation and said, "I was there at that pub lots of times, but the problem is that when you go to those places, if people are with friends or in a group, no one knows who is available and wanting to meet someone else." David heartily agreed.

Eventually he plucked up the courage to phone Katie's number but she wasn't in, so he blurted out a message on her answer machine. When she heard it, she didn't know what to do. She admitted to being terribly nervous. Her sister was there and said, "Well, you'll have to phone him back." "No, no, I can't. I'll wait for him to phone me again." To which her outgoing, vivacious sister said, "No, you must return the call. I'll phone him and pretend to be you." So with no more ado her sister promptly telephoned David.

"How David ever agreed to meet me afterwards I'll never know because conversations after that first one were so different; another voice, different answers to questions and, of course, a completely different personality." David apparently was only told about Katie's sister quite a long time afterwards.

They decided to meet at the one place they both knew, The Beacon Hotel. Katie said, "I knew there and then that I was going to spend the rest of my life with this man. I just knew it."

What David could not get over in those first conversations was that they knew the same people and the same areas. He said, "I was completely mesmerised by the whole situation. I had even noticed Katie's father's farm when I was doing some blacksmithing down their lane. I'd said to myself, "That's a tidy farm," and had taken in the location and everything, really just at the time in my life when I felt the most alone." Over the months their families met and they all got on well. Both sets of parents were traditional hard working people who had come through the trials and tribulations that all couples go through and had still stayed together. It was a big issue for Katie when it was decided that David should come and live with her, as she was a Church Warden and both sets of parents were churchgoers there were moral issues to be considered. But they both, more strongly than words can tell, felt that this was right. And so they moved in together.

The marriage ceremony was the most magical experience in their lives. Over a second cool drink I was told of the true country feeling they created in everything to do with the wedding. David looked very dashing in a formal morning suit and Katie's dress represented fields of corn. Bridesmaids were dressed in similar shimmering deep cream and gold and everyone had yellow and cream flowers.

Katie walked to the small country church down the lane which was crowded with local people from her parents' home only a few yards from the church. The transport back to the reception marquee on the lawns was on a richly garlanded harvest trailer pulled by a scrupulously clean tractor. The wedding feast was a country hog roast. This suited everyone.

They said to me that their love was perfect but virtually immediately after their wedding it was to be tested because David lost his job. The challenges of married life had begun and they existed on Katie's salary which made everything very tight and difficult. One night Katie happened to be telling the vicar that life was a bit of a struggle and before she left he handed her the church magazine. That night, looking through the magazine, they saw an advert for the job that David went on to obtain. "That job seemed to come out of heaven," they echoed, "Just when we needed it most."

As I talked to them that afternoon I found Katie and David to be amazingly similar in all respects, even down to their build, both being rounder rather than angular. They are both emotional people who cry easily. They work hard and have exactly the same values in life. I suppose you could say they are on the same wavelength.

With the new job, a new house was the next thing. They are the first to admit it is quite small, but it is cosy, and it is their own, together. As the saying goes 'New house new baby' and that is exactly what happened. In due course a perfect little baby boy was born.

2
Little Dolly Daydream

Driving back from Gloucestershire I decided on impulse to call into Redditch, the town where I grew up. As I was pottering about, wondering at all the changes, I spotted our old house in the window of an estate agent. I just had to go and have a look at it and made up a story to the estate agent about looking for a property to do up for investment. They seemed very busy at the time and asked would I mind having the key and showing myself around as no one was living in the house. I was delighted to comply and dared not show my real excitement at this opportunity to walk alone around the house I was brought up in but had not seen for forty years.

It was very nostalgic to go back to a place with so many important childhood experiences and memories. Everywhere seemed much smaller than it had when I was a child. The garden I remembered as being so long it seemed to take five minutes to run the full length was in fact only about 100 yards from end to end. The enormous tree that grew wonderful Worcester apples and from which I would sling my hammock to the old wash house, looked now like any mundane tree of ordinary proportions!

I went from room to room and vivid memories came jumping out at me. I saw images of scenes that had happened in every corner throughout the many years of family life there.

Our house was in a row of similar houses in the town. When you went up or down the road both ends had much nicer bay windows, with ornate brickwork and welcoming little porches that made them look exceedingly superior to ours. It was a basic, un-modernized, workingman's house of the late nineteenth century. Two bedrooms were on the first floor and a rather frightening large attic stretched over them both. All the rooms except my bedroom had dull, nondescript wallpaper with doors and paintwork in dark brown. The floors everywhere were brown stained wooden floor boards covered with home made rugs.

There was, of course, no central heating. My mother would carry a shovel full of lighted coals upstairs from the main living room fire, which would quickly become a small roaring ball of flames in the little black leaded and ornate bedroom grate. Nowadays if you are lucky enough to have an open fire somewhere in the house you would not dare to precariously balance red hot embers on a small shovel and carry them over the inevitable fitted carpets. One trip or off balanced moment would tip the burning coals all over the expensive floor coverings.

I was an only child and spent hours alone in my bedroom. I was always short for my age, well built and sturdy. My foremost feature was a plump rosy face and I was always smiling. With my round, open, happy face I am told I gave the impression of having a friendly nature, which I suppose I did tend to have. However I felt quite shy most of the time. My face was topped by a mass of tight curly blond hair, a bit like Shirley Temple from the neck up but hopefully without the precocious personality that she must have had.

Matchmaking was a passion even when I was a very small child and I always had an inner inexplicable feeling that I would eventually, given the chance, be good at it. My other dream from early childhood was to belong to a farming way of life, being part of the working life of the English countryside.

My room was painted a lovely bright duck egg blue and I spent long hours there playing with my dolls, as small girls do, or used to before computers and television. One of my very earliest memories is lining up the dolls, some girls and some boys, and matching them up as lifelong partners. The dolls were of course a mixed bag. I had one very beautiful Rosebud doll, with auburn curls and a blue checked frock with matching knickers, white ankle socks and shoes with a strap and button. Next down from this paragon were two of a similar nature but missing some items of clothing or wearing hand-knits. Then there was my old teddy bear, a golliwog, a stuffed dog, a Welsh doll with a leg missing and several peg dolls. If I was short of partners I used to get a peg from the basket and make someone up. Perhaps a dark gentleman with a moustache or a lady with full red lips. In this way, everyone ended up with someone. I think the characteristics I imagined in those early days were quite simple. Some would be tall or short and those with fair hair were matched with other fair headed dollies. The chatty ones would be put with the same and the quiet ones would be paired off together. I do not remember their characters being more sophisticated or complicated than this.

My father had an old typewriter which he left in the attic above the bedrooms and hardly ever used. I would meticulously and laboriously type out the dolls' names and put down who I was matching them with, and why. My father came to the attic one day to type out some letters to find not one piece of paper left. He was so cross with me that I had to avoid him for days.

It was obvious to me even then that matchmaking was going to be a lifelong passion.

I suppose, looking back on all this now, I could have been considered an odd child in respect of my practice of pairing dolls with one another for marriage. This was definitely not normal for a little girl. Where this obsession came from originally, who knows. Most children brought up in the 1940s and 50s certainly lived with a mother and father and looking back, as with millions of other children at this time, I could not have visualized any other type of life. My parents lived happily together although looking back there were still remnants of the strain of getting through the war years. mother and father married after war had been declared. They were right in thinking that father might have to go away and that is why they married so quickly and so young. For several years he had to work in London without my mother, and then through an accident, ended up in hospital for a considerable period of time. Being parted like this put chinks of uncertainty and doubt between them and it took, as with many other couples at this time, I suspect, a very long time to overcome this. But by the time they had got to the 1950s all seemed to be harmonious between them and their marriage and my life were happy.

I suppose in my young and naive beginnings the contentment in their marriage would have made me feel that this was the life for which anyone should aim. I therefore tried to create the same for my dolls and it strengthened my dream of carrying it on for other people. Now, of course, I am deeply respectful of any style of life that an individual feels is right for them. Many times, while talking to someone who is very lonely and feels desperate to meet a partner, I have been known to say, 'You are happy to a certain extent now although you feel lonely. It is better to remain that way than bring someone totally inappropriate into your life and end up still lonely and dreadfully unhappy.'

Besides matching up my dolls, which was a good winter pursuit, I used to get enormous pleasure from being outside in any sort of rural environment. I loved to run down through our garden and straight into a vast maze of unused allotments. They had reverted to wilderness after the war and were full of interesting derelict wooden huts, fruit bushes, apple trees and overgrown hedges that surrounded little squares of land. They had obviously at one time been the allotment holders' pride and joy and I don't know why they had been largely abandoned. They were criss-crossed with pathways, where you could imagine men pushing their wheelbarrows full of home grown fruit and vegetables back to their homes. Two or three little streams and ponds had developed with frog spawn turning eventually into masses of tadpoles.

This land was my salvation from the back-to-back living of my home, because I craved space and the open air. I played here for hours, usually by myself but sometimes with neighbouring children. I had a particular grassy spot where I would run to, from the house, without stopping. It was the highest point where, when you sat down, you could look over a big expanse of open land. You could breathe the fresh air wafting from the woods over by the golf course that you could see in the distance.

I would sit on this little hillock for a while and look out over the view. From here you could also observe virtually every patchwork square of the allotments so if I saw someone walking through 'my land' I would traverse the streams and pathways and weave my way through the hedges to spy on whoever was there. I strongly felt they should not be there. It was mine and I thought no one else knew this ground like me. I'm not sure if that was the case but even now, a full fifty years on, if you transported me back and dropped me in the maze of hedgerows and trees I 'm sure I could find my way back to civilization, with no faltering or hesitation.

As an only child I did not expect, as a right, to be constantly playing with others but learnt different ways of keeping myself occupied. Much of my playing time would be on my own watching neighbours and visitors to the allotments. Perhaps my practice in those days of quietly surveying adults going about their business gradually built up my understanding of people and situations to give me my matchmaking skills.

Redditch had always been a small industrial town and in the early 1950s it had not changed much from before the war. Although I hated the closed in grimy feel when I visited the factory where my dad ran his small business I still found it fascinating. He processed surgical needles and fishing hooks with metal heat treatments. I used to sit in the little office and tidy his desk while looking through into the workshop at the hardening furnaces. There was a constant smell of hot oil everywhere. The workshop consisted of three roaring fires, open at the front and quite similar to a baker's oven but with a tremendous amount of heat and flames darting dangerously out. Dad would put the surgical needles or fishing hooks in the different ovens, according to the temperature required. He used very long handled metal implements but still he would be constantly sweating profusely with the tremendous heat and he wore just his greasy trousers and vest. Oily steam would burst out into the atmosphere from big vats as he put the red-hot needles into the reservoir of oil to cool. Metal heat treatment was hard work and as it was his own business he would work from seven to seven every day, except Sunday. The business had been in the family for three generations so I suppose it was important to him to continue working it.

Because of the lack of money my mother worked from home making fishing tackle. Redditch's main industries at this time were the manufacture of surgical needles and fishing hooks. She had her little worktable under the living room window and, using real cat gut, she would tie tiny pretty coloured feathers in various different combinations onto little fishing hooks. It was meticulous work. You had to complete hundreds and hundreds to earn two pounds ten shillings. About forty hours work.

I got an underlying impression from my parents that to succeed in life you not only had to work hard but also definitely to work for yourself, run your own business and be in command of your own destiny. It was pointed out that dad's business had prospects but the work mum did would never get her or any of us anywhere. They were right because by the mid fifties father had expanded to buying a new factory and bought massive all electric furnaces. At last he would not be working so very hard shovelling huge amounts of coal into the open furnaces every twenty minutes. A task he had been doing, except for the war years, since he was fifteen. Mum stopped her fishing tackle and started working for dad, and at last we did have prospects.

Carpets were bought, our first vacuum cleaner was purchased and I had a new bed. The dolls were consigned to the attic, but not my dreams. As I sat deep in my thoughts on my little grassy spot overlooking the allotments, it came to me that self employed status was the only one for me. It didn't occur to me that I could achieve this by indulging the pleasure I got from matchmaking. I suppose there is only so much a ten year old can piece together.

My parents did not harbour the same love of the open outdoors as I did. They actually could not abide the countryside. But my father's father, Grandfather Victor, was a farmer and from as early as I could remember I would go to stay at his small farm located in the lush green rolling Worcestershire countryside between Stratford upon Avon and Worcester close to the small village of Flyford Flavel. Grandfather Victor was a short man, rotund in body and plump in the face, with a lovely soft unweathered complexion. He would wear the most bedraggled and worn out clothes whilst doing his farm work. Like many farmers he always put his clothes together with pieces of string either holding up or wrapped around or entwined through his coats and trousers. The trousers would also be held up with belt and braces with the waist being (Benny Hill style) virtually in line with his armpits. When he went off the farm, however, he would struggle to do up a tight corset, placed over his white long johns. He would lean on the dressing table with a face full of agony as he huffed and puffed to bring the hooks and eyes together. There would be a massive show of relief on his face in the mirror when the last hook was secured. However, I suspect the relief was just facial for any heavy exhaling of breath might have resulted in all the tension dramatically bursting open. Even from such a young age I seemed to know all this exertion was to hold his tummy in, but I never knew if grandfather realised I used to spy on him and watch this fascinating performance through the slit in the bedroom door. He would then don the smartest of suits, accompanied by his trilby hat, and drive off in his famous Jaguar car. With him being so short, it looked, for all the world, as if a dwarf was at the wheel.

My grandmother was an old fashioned lady. It is awful to think that my abiding memory of her is emptying the pots from under the beds every morning, with a 'slop' bucket and a rinsing bucket that was taken from bedroom to bedroom in the farmhouse. I would spend days helping her gather berries and fruit for her bottling and sheep's wool to put around her bunions. She would never go outdoors without a large straw hat, which usually had a mass of cherries perched precariously, decorating the one side. Like grandfather, she was short and plump with enormous arms, which were so good to snuggle down into at the end of the day. I was fascinated by the occasional glimpse of her voluminous shiny pink bloomers that were slightly revealed when she tucked her hankie up one leg. Her farm attire was the complete opposite to her going out dress, which would be floral or have white spots on a blue background. With a belt at the waist her large bosom would be dramatically emphasised and her hips would seem to span a doorway and a half. She would always look ultra pristine, sparklingly crisp and clean with a pair of spotless white gloves either worn or carried.

I used to help grandfather with his sheep, poultry and pigs and would spend hours mending fences, pumping water from old gravity water pumps, watching little pigs snuggle together under warm lamps and gathering eggs. I loved the life on the farm and would beg to spend most of my weekends and all of the school holidays there. In comparison to the built up location of my home not far from industrial Redditch, it was paradise.

My mass of curly blond hair looked from afar like a halo around my head. I was, however, far from an angel most of the time and I was always getting into scrapes and predicaments when I was staying at my grandparents' farm. Sometimes, because of the naughty things I had done, I would hide for hours in the stable in the top field. Here you could watch the house to see if someone was coming to find you. One of my sins was caused by my passion for tinned condensed milk. I think it was still rationed in the 1950s but I would run off with a tin to the far end of the farm and with two holes made in the top, you could suck out the most delicious nectar in the world.

I would be grandfather's constant companion and even when I was very young he would talk about his life to me, particularly his decision to have a small farm. He detested Redditch, where we all originated from, and at the very earliest opportunity he bought his farm. You could tell it was everything in life he ever wanted as he appeared to me to be a truly happy man, always laughing with a smile for everyone.

I now realise that grandfather made an immense impression on me as a child. I suspect his influence only really nurtured a deep seated innermost feeling of the love of space and the open air that maybe had been there in my genes for generations. Others who have gone into our family history have told me that we were affluent sheep farmers in Cornwall in the fifteenth and sixteenth century. Perhaps this could explain my desire for open spaces, to be close to the earth and the sea.

The only time I actually saw grandfather angry was one day when he had been told by his oldest daughter that her husband was about to leave her. His immense rage was immediately obvious and he left the farmhouse with his shotgun under his arm to 'kill the bastard.' My grandmother was terrified as she watched him start to walk over the fields in the direction of where my auntie lived. Grandmother telephoned my father and he seemed to arrive at the farm very quickly and he went running over the fields in the direction of my auntie's house. Being the nosey little girl I was I wanted to witness all the drama that would take place. The only way I could catch up on the activity was to ride the small horse, Flicker, that was kept as a pet on the farm and catch up with them across the fields. Flicker and I hid behind a hedge and saw my father disarming grandfather of the family shotgun a few yards before he was about to enter his daughter's house. My father did not allow that shotgun back at my grandfather's farm for several years.

One of my aunties' married a farmer when I was six years old. The farm she moved to was large for those days, with an enormous and very old farmhouse with a large duck pond in the farm yard. I would go and stay there some weekends. The day would be spent collecting, cleaning and packing hundreds upon hundreds of eggs. The hens were all free range and had many fields available for them to scratch around. The problem was these fields had lots of trees in them and one was like a small orchard with apple trees everywhere. Every evening seemed to be spent shaking the trees vigorously or even using clothes props to poke the roosting hens down to the ground, then herding them, clucking, flapping and protesting wildly into their houses, where they would eventually settle down and become silent.

When the milking was finished we'd all have supper with about fifteen around the table; family, workers and friends. I relished the talk around that kitchen table of the countryside and farming.

By the time I had got into my dreamy teenage years I would visualize living on a quite isolated farm, working hand in hand with my husband, building a good farming life together. He would be a 'salt of the earth' farmer and in my young romantic imagination I would picture him as a replica of John Ridd in 'Lorna Doone.' I had read a children's version of the book some time before and when it was serialized on television I was glued to the screen and watched every episode on a Sunday afternoon. My hero, John Ridd, was played by Bill Travers and I fell in love there and then with his strong manly build and brown bushy beard.

I talked of and giggled about the future with my girl friends and described, as young girls do, what I wished for in life. I would tell them that my husband would be broad and masculine in build and that we'd have lots of children. When I told them I wanted him to be a farmer, they couldn't understand how anyone would want this sort of life. In their eyes sophistication and excitement were surely the main aims for everyone and they were convinced you couldn't get that by living on a farm. So these rural dreams were quickly knocked off the reality shelf by my girl friends' feelings that they knew what was best for me.

At about this time I would go to the library in Redditch and bring back books on matchmaking. Books relating to the Jewish community and how their matchmaking took place and about the role of matchmaking in arranged marriages in eastern countries or anything else I could get my hands on regarding this subject. I suppose the next stage after pairing up dolls was considering how it was really done in the grown up world. I was so intrigued by what I felt was the romance of matchmaking that I remember thinking, "One day I want to do that."

I was always interested in people and would read books on the psychology of relationships. I really enjoyed getting to know others. I liked talking with people on a one to one basis. I would get off a bus and during the journey would have got to know the life story of the stranger sitting next to me. Looking back I think my mother used to worry that I got too involved with people who were complete strangers. In the 1950s the dangerous consequences of talking to strangers were not emphasized as they are now. Certainly my mother never seriously warned me against it. She just thought me rather odd, I think.

As with all adolescents the crunch time comes when you really have to decide what your future career will be and because I had not got the courage of my convictions I literally did what my parents wanted me to do. That was to train as a registered nurse. I did dare to suggest psychology, but that was laughed at as being a ridiculous option.

Initially I obtained a place to train at the Queen Elizabeth's Hospital in Birmingham. After my initial interview I realized I would hate being in such a large city so I decided to go to a smaller place and trained as a student nurse at Worcester Royal Infirmary. As soon as I got off duty, especially when I'd been on nights, I could not wait to go for a spin in my little black Morris Minor car. On one such occasion I persuaded my two best friends, Jenny and Angela, to join me and we whizzed out to the Malvern Hills. Unfortunately, a wheel came loose and we ended up in a ditch with the three of us receiving minor injuries. We felt pretty embarrassed that morning to arrive back in casualty in an ambulance, on stretchers, exactly from where we had been on duty all the previous night. Before even being discharged from casualty we were summoned to attend Matron's office and subsequently given a severe reprimand on motoring around the countryside without any sleep.

I enjoyed training to be a nurse. I loved getting to know people and picked up a lot about how to talk to people in all situations. I learnt the usual pleasantries for polite conversation which we all use on the surface. But also, of course, as all nurses and doctors do, you learn how to cope when coming face to face with people who are dealing with the most difficult traumas of their lives. When you are young you think that life is all black and white, but nursing sick people you learn so very quickly that it is not. There are so many grey areas that we have to accept and that we are all individuals, each with our own qualities and faults. Little do you realise how these early life experiences are preparing you for later life. Without my nursing I know my whole approach and attitude to my matchmaking would have been different.

One evening after finishing work on the wards I decided to drive home to my parents as I had several days off. It was quite late into the evening, dark, cold and raining. About three miles outside Worcester my Morris Minor stopped and I suspected I had run out of petrol. There were no houses or a telephone box in sight. I had no alternative but to start walking back the way I came. It was pitch black and I had no umbrella or even a jacket. I put my head down and trudged along the side of the road, feeling very cold, wet and miserable and sorry for myself. After a while a red car came around the corner and very nearly ran into me but stopped a few yards on. The driver got out and shouted, "Is that your damn car around that corner? I nearly drove straight into it!" I think I was near to tears at this point and when he realised I'd run out of petrol, his annoyance subsided and he offered me a lift to a garage. He then realised he could after all be my knight in shining armour and save me from a difficult predicament by suggesting he brought me back to my car with the petrol. He poured the petrol in to my car, made sure it started and then promptly asked me out on a date; I married him about eighteen months later.

Mark was a city man, confident and strong minded and I think these features attracted me to him. He enjoyed the 'cut and thrust' of business ventures and ran his own garage. I was still working as a nurse but my heart wasn't in it as I longed to have children and be a full time mother at home. Months of our marriage went by and I did not become pregnant. Natural instinct told me that it would be best to find a fulfilling challenge. I thought about starting an introduction agency, but I suppose I was still not mature enough to do what I really wanted to do no matter what anyone else thought. The idea of matchmaking as a serious business in England was completely alien at that time. Introduction agencies were considered embarrassing, in bad taste and a last resort for those who didn't have enough about them to find their own mate.

I knew I wanted to come out of nursing, maybe just for a while, but I did want other challenges to come my way, even if it could not be matchmaking. Quite quickly after this I recognised a good venture, a business enterprise that to me stood out. I'd heard about a newly built church complex a short distance from where I lived. It had a large hall and about six different rooms leading off with a reception area, toilets, kitchen and several large enclosed areas outside and it was not used at all during the week. I put in an offer for the rent of the premises with the wish to start a children's nursery school. The Church Authorities agreed and Worcester City Council passed my plans. After a few months of getting everything together for the nursery I opened and five children were brought along on the first day. Within a few months I was employing five ladies and a trained teacher. Children came from all over the city and it was soon open all day, five days a week with a waiting list of seventy children.

It was a lucky opportunity, to establish a successful business where there was no competition; private nursery schools in the late 1960s and early 1970s were virtually unheard of. I was twenty three years old and employing ladies ten or twenty years older than myself. It brought out all the lessons I'd learnt from generally helping in my fathers' office, particularly in taking on and employing people and the paper work necessary to run an efficient business. Experiences that I did not realise I was picking up in earlier years came flowing back.

I eventually sold the nursery as a going concern after being offered a very nice sum. I invested the money in my husband's business and started working in partnership with him. But at this point destiny shaped my life and the culmination of events that at the time were very sad slowly turned my life around towards a direction I'd always really wanted. This sadness came about in the ending of my marriage in my late twenties. Throughout all of our time together we had very much wanted to have a child, but it just did not happen. Our parting became inevitable when another woman came into my husband's life and she quickly became pregnant. The pain of the loss of him and our marriage and the child that I so much wanted but that he was going to have by another woman was so deep, dreadful and despairing that I found myself sinking down into depression caused by the awful feelings of utter rejection.

I tried very hard, however, to see the positive aspects of this change in my life and decided eventually that the one feature I could hold on to was that now I could decide to do things for the first time totally to please myself. I was still suffering insurmountable sorrow but I vowed that I would never again live in a town or city and that I would spend the rest of my life in the country. I was able to rent a perfect little cottage for £5 a week from Jenny, a good friend from my nursing days. She and her husband were going to America for two years. Amazingly it was deep in the countryside at St. Owen's Cross not far from Ross on Wye, in Herefordshire, the county that I had always loved. I knew so well the mystical valleys adjoining the Welsh border, where time seems to stand still and where, as you come upon the Llantony Abbey, you are taken back into a medieval age. You can climb onto the hilltops and explore your way over to Hay on Wye and be transfixed at the wonder of such magnificent landscapes. You can take pleasure in the architecture, visualising the people and events that took place amongst the black and white buildings of the villages in the northern part of the county.

The cottage was about half a mile up a dirt track off a quiet lane. The small area was called Chapel Tump and apparently in the eighteen century there would be illegal chapel meetings in the garden of the cottage, attended by the good country folk of the area. It was quite extraordinary to sit there and think of the absolute faith and courage that these dissenters had shown all those many years ago as they gathered there.

The cottage had an orchard and quite a lot of ground all around it where I kept chickens. There were a few neighbouring cottages in the locality but no one close. I loved being there but sometimes I would go for days without seeing a soul and I eventually became very lonely. I was lonely for general company and lonely for a 'mate.' Some nights for months and months I would cry myself to sleep hoping the next day I would wake up wishing to start a new day with hope and enthusiasm. But for many months this did not happen and at times I know I reached pits of despair that seemed impossible to struggle out of thinking about my marriage break up. I suppose I could not believe it had happened and I was travelling through a combination of emotions covering shock, disbelief, emptiness and finally facing up to the breakdown of my marriage.

When I talk to people whose marriages have broken up and they are despairing of the future, I can say, "I know how you feel, I've been there. Truly I have." Although it is now over twenty five years ago, you never forget.

Gradually after a few months I was able to be a little braver towards life in general and managed to attend various short and part time courses at the local agricultural college. I was amazed that after a few months I really started to enjoy attending and after getting some minor qualifications in farm record keeping I decided to get a place to do a full time two year course to qualify as a farm secretary.

This full time course would not start for about nine months. I realized this was a good time to get the travel bug out of my system. My aim was to return for the beginning of the full time farm secretarial course in September.

I had always wanted to see the Far East but to just jump on a plane seemed far too easy. I wanted to traverse the continents and arrive in India having seen many countries. I got to know several individuals who were doing this trip around the same time as me and spoke with many who had done it before. So, with much information and promises to try to meet others on the way, I set off. I travelled mostly by rail and stopped in hostels as I went through Europe. Once I'd reached Austria I started camping where I could and if I liked a place I would just stop there for weeks at a time. Eventually I arrived in Turkey. I fell in love with this country and was amazed at its vastness. I spent days visiting Roman ruins then relaxing for a week at a time by rivers and waterfalls.

I did get attacked whilst sleeping under the stars in Eastern Turkey but thankfully the man ran away in fright when I screamed out very loud. I loved going to sleep looking at the night sky, although I'm not sure if I would do it now. I still love watching the stars but with maturity I would see so many dangers in this way of life. It's a good thing that in youth, you don't see these risks and therefore do many more things when you are younger.

By the time it came to travelling through Iran I had loosely joined up with other Brits. It was good at last to meet others older than me and two of the men were in their fifties. Most of the people I had come across previously were teenagers who seemed out to smoke as much 'pot' as they could. I've never participated in this so at times would feel a bit out on a limb.

Iran was precarious as I just arrived there when the Shah of Persia was being deposed and there was revolution, fighting, unrest and gunfire everywhere. It was hair-raising to travel through the country but I joined up with other Brits and we gave each other support and the courage to carry on. But my roaming and exploring came to a sudden halt when my new found friends and I found ourselves in a very dangerous situation in Afghanistan with another revolution in full swing. We soon realised it was truly best to 'get the hell out of there' for the gun fire and tanks were all around us. We stuck it out for many days thinking it would subside. In the end we just caught whatever plane we could to get out of it all and ended up back home, regretfully without finishing the trip I'd planned to India.

So, returning to Britain earlier than expected meant I did not experience and explore as many countries of the world as I had wished, but I did come home safe and sound.

After a week or two of getting used to sleeping in a bed again and not ducking and diving from tanks and snipers or looking for insects in my shoes in the morning, my thoughts turned back to what I was going to do until my farm secretarial course started. I decided to take only jobs that appealed to me that would be temporary and would take me to various parts of Britain. My only condition was that anywhere I worked would have to be in the countryside.

I noticed a job going in Staffordshire. A person was needed to get all the bookwork up to date on a farm and look after two small children whilst their mother was in hospital. 'I think I could do that," I said to myself, and was offered it immediately when I applied. This was my first excursion to live in the north. Little did I know that I would never return to live in Worcestershire and that I would learn to love another part of England just as much.

I knew this job would be good experience before I started my farm secretarial course. The farm books had been untouched for so long. The children were sweet and I greatly enjoyed their company. Their grandmother would come to take over from me on my days off and I would always try to have those days away from the farm. Staffordshire surprised me with its diversity and for the first time I enjoyed the desolate and windswept moor lands in the north of the county. It was on one of those days off that I decided to attend a local farm sale. Quite a lot of small items from the farmhouse were being sold that I was interested in.

I looked around but, as sometimes happens at auctions, the catalogue had misleading descriptions of some of the items and I could not get interested in anything for sale. My car was parked quite a long way off and suddenly the heavens opened. I was lucky to be able to duck for cover in a nearby shed. As I dived in I glimpsed a man also sheltering out of the downpour that had come on so quickly.

We spoke, of course, of the dreadful weather and gazed out at the rain which was deafening as it beat down on the corrugated roof. The roof was also leaking quite extensively so we stood there with coat collars high around us still getting damp. We started to discuss the auction generally and I thought we were both not paying any attention to each other, just looking out at this deluge of rain. Then he started asking me about where I was working and a bit about myself, and we passed the time of day as sociably as we could under the circumstances.

He said he lived near Bakewell in Derbyshire and very often came back Staffordshire way as he'd been brought up in the locality and knew it well. I told him I'd never been to Bakewell but understood it to be a lovely market town. "Come over," he said, "Let's meet up and I'll show you around." He asked for my telephone number so we could arrange a meeting and as he finished writing the numbers on his farm catalogue I looked up into his face for the first time. His coat collar fell aside and stopped shielding him from the dripping rain, revealing a bushy brown beard! I was instantly transfixed; then, as he turned and was walking out to leave the shed, he said, "By the way, my name's John, what's yours?"

I couldn't even utter a goodbye to him as I was rooted to the spot with an overpowering reaction in the pit of my stomach. A quiver shot down my spine and I thought - 'What's happening?' Here, in the middle of the

Staffordshire moors, in a muddy wet cowshed I had bumped into the image of my romantic adolescent dreams, John Ridd himself. I thought I must be dreaming.

But I wasn't. John contacted me a few days later and he suggested he drive out to where I was and we'd have a drink at a local pub (I thought we were to meet for him to show me Bakewell, but never mind, I thought). I really had to look at him for the first time as I had not paid that much attention or been able to see him clearly in the dingy shed. He was tallish with such a kind and appealing smile and with quite a mass of curly brown hair. His glasses added character to his roundish face. He was broad and masculine and he had that fantastic beard! I suppose I looked at him then in the same manner as anyone meeting someone through the Bureau for the first time.

I learnt that he was an avid reader and we talked to each other about the recent books we had read. I asked him what his favourite book was and that same overpowering and amazing reaction came tingling down my spine when he answered, "Well if you consider all the books I've ever read, I'd have to say 'Lorna Doone'."

Every word he said seemed uncanny and pointing towards a providence that had caused us to come together.

We had a really lovely time that evening and when it was time to go our separate ways John asked if he could see me again. Of course I was delighted - a dairy farmer who looked like John Ridd and made my stomach turn somersaults - what more could I ask? I was about to suggest that we might meet up the following Saturday perhaps for a picnic, when he said, "Of course, I'll have to get the hay in before I can see you again, so it may be a week or two, depending on the weather. I hope you don't mind." Well, what could I say? And thus began a lifetime of playing second fiddle to a farm.

John was a very decisive man who, when he made his mind up over something, really did everything to obtain what he wanted. Within a short while he asked me to marry him. One evening he asked me twice and on a particular Sunday he asked me three times. I have to admit it was not too romantic. He said he could not 'court' me over the winter, as being a livestock farmer he would be very committed in those winter months with much work. "Our relationship will never last over these months with you so far away. With me working all the hours I have to I'd never find time to see you," he said. "Marry me now, soon before winter. September will do."

I still intended at that stage to take up my place at agricultural college but realised very quickly that I had a very big decision to make. Yes, it was the lifestyle I had always wanted but that should not be the most important consideration; it should be the person you are marrying. Also when you have had one marriage end and the utter grief that gives, you don't want to go through it again. But I did say yes, and I have never regretted it and I never did take up that place at college.

We settled down to married life together and decided quite soon to start a family. If only it was as easy to make a baby as it is to say 'Yes, we'll have one.' After a year of trying still nothing happened. We went into a period of temperature taking, medical consultations, tests, infertility drugs - we investigated them all. Eventually the consultant said for us to 'Just go away and forget about making babies for a while.' He said we should do something 'challenging, interesting, something that you've always wanted to do, take your mind off it all' and as I drove home I thought continuously about his advice.

Recently John had employed two young lads to help with the farmwork. He had always done his own bookwork and felt he wanted to continue doing most of it himself, so there wasn't much I could do on the farm.

I sat at the kitchen table that evening weighing things up and thinking about what the consultant had said and gradually my thoughts came together and my resolve hardened until I found myself shouting out loud, "Yes, I'm going to do what I've always wanted to do - I'm going to start a marriage bureau just for farmers." I was in fact shocked as well as delighted to realise that I could consider realistically fulfilling my lifelong ambition - and very grateful for fate that had made it rain that day on the Staffordshire Moors.

3
The Farmer Wants a Wife

That same evening, after John had finished milking, I told him that the consultant had said, "Go home, do something interesting and challenging and take your mind off making babies for a while, and in time it might all happen." Then I waited a while until he'd finished his meal and settled down to be comfortable. I took a deep breath and spoke of my plans to start a matchmaking agency for farmers and country people.

Well, to be honest, he just fell about with mirth and amazement, "A dating agency! Eh Pat, my darling, it'll never work, farmers using a marriage bureau! Eh, you'll not get farmers doing anything like that, never in a million years."

Well, I hadn't expected immediate agreement, but this time I was much more determined after my success with the nursery school. I knew I could run a good business and I knew I was still passionate about matchmaking. In fact, it didn't take long for John to realise that it would probably be a good thing to do and he admitted that if anyone could make a success of such a venture, it would be me. That was good enough. It would have been great to have had more enthusiasm, but never mind. To get his agreement was enough for now.

That was in the autumn of 1981. By the early spring of 1982 I had made plans about how I would do the matching of couples and prepared a business plan. I borrowed fifty pounds from the farm account to pay for my brochures to be printed. To this day John still jokingly reminds me that I've never paid it back.

I can remember the face of the printer when I presented my first brochure design and a mock up of my registration form. He was an old man who I think had never, ever come across the concept of a marriage bureau so he could not grasp the idea at all. Tentatively I submitted by post the wording for my advertising to the Farmers Guardian newspaper. When I telephoned their office to see about the cost and paying for the advert they said they would have to think about it, as they had never accepted an advert like this before. I then approached the Farmers Weekly. Very quickly I was told they would not accept such 'personal' advertising. Was I an escort agency, they asked? I know they thought I could even be worse, you could tell. They wanted to ask 'was I on the game?' They did not put it into actual words but I know they were thinking about it after the conversation I had with them. But to my great relief, after two weeks of consideration, the Farmers Guardian accepted my first advert. All this seems odd today when you see all the personal adverts in the papers.

The only other specialised agency in the country at the time was one in London for Asian people. There were a few other general agencies, virtually all based in London, but you could literally count them on one hand. Dateline was the biggest and Heather Jenner's Marriage Bureau was the longest established. There was, however, no one specialising in country people.

I could have surreptitiously sent off for brochures and forms from these agencies but I purposely did not do that, as I wanted to do things my way and not be influenced by others. To me it was so important that farming and country people had questions posed and methods of matching developed to suit them and their particular lifestyles. I felt general agencies could not possibly take into consideration the unique and very diverse aspects of a country lifestyle.

Before anyone joined the Bureau I practised several trial runs on matching people up. Would their education be the most important aspect, or background, type of work or age? I realised quite quickly that you would never be able to say absolutely what the single most important compatible factor for everyone is. With most I thought it would be location and age. Of course there were no computers then so my basic office equipment consisted of a phone, a typewriter and carbon copy paper. My fees in 1982 were twenty pounds for eight Introductions. Wow! Those were the days.

I crossed my fingers in the last week of May 1982 when on the Friday of that week my first advert came out. At lunchtime on the Sunday I had a phone enquiry. Could they have a brochure and before I knew it in the following week I'd received numerous enquiries. I quickly sent my brochures out and by the next Friday, June 1982, people had started sending in their registration forms and joining up.

As with all new businesses you have to have a bit of luck and mine came in the way the new members joined. They could have been all males or all females, with no age group being represented twice to give any chance of a match but luckily it worked out equally spread. People in their thirties were most common and amazingly the sexes were roughly the same in numbers. Very quickly I was able to match people up, write to them regarding each other and complete my first introductions. I couldn't really believe that I was at last fulfilling my long-held childhood dream.

Quite honestly I thought I would only run the Bureau for a short while until I became pregnant. Then I had no doubt I would close it down and concentrate on family life. However eventually John and I had to face up to the fact that we were not going to have our own children, no matter how hard we or the doctors tried and we decided to complete our family through adoption.

In 1982 a most lovely little boy of two years was placed with us and we adopted him. He was gorgeous and lovable and the most precious person in our lives. Matthew enjoyed outdoor life and the farm and we were all set to complete our family with a second child in the future. When he was only five our darling little boy had a fatal accident. We had only had him for three years. There are no words to describe the utter despair you feel on losing a child. You want to stop living so you don't have to feel the immense and unbearable pain.

With time, however, we came to look forward again, and we adopted a robust and smiling little baby boy who we named Ben. Just under two years after that our pretty baby daughter Sarah came to live with us at five months and we adopted her too.

When we did start having the children I decided I should start to employ some staff to help me. My first full time lady was Anne, a local farmer's daughter. Anne was such a versatile and adaptable person and the arrangement was that her main work would be in the Bureau office, but any time I needed someone to look after Matthew and then Ben, whilst I was in the office, she would baby sit as well. Anne concentrated on the admin work with me doing all the matching of couples and client interviews. By the time Sarah arrived in 1987 I had taken on my second secretary, Mary.

Life around the summer of 1987 was hectic. I had two children below the age of two and the Bureau was getting busier as each month went by. The only time I would have to myself would be if I got up early in the morning, when John would get up to milk which he would always do at four thirty am.

I loved to walk down the farm drive at this early hour and through the lush fields close to the house. I would always keep the house in sight as the two babies would still be fast asleep in their cots. The fields would be heavy with the grass that would make our silage crop and feed our cows throughout the winter. There is nothing more wonderful than early morning birdsong which nearly deafens you as you walk through the trees. The variety of sounds would almost take my breath away. Those walks would rejuvenate me for the day's work ahead which would be full of the complexities of dealing with people and their longings to meet someone special, bringing up two small children, having a busy farmhouse and running the local toddler group. I needed to breathe in the beginning of the new day with its distinctive freshness and watch the steady arrival of the sun slowly creeping above the horizon. I would think of the joy of having such longed for children and I would declare to myself and the woods and the fields that life was good.

As I walked back towards the farmhouse I would look over to the east where you can see some of the glorious valleys of the district. The Lathkill Dale and Bradford Dale with the limestone walls skirting around rocky outcrops, dotted with trees and speckled with grazing sheep.

Passing our garden in those early summer days, I would be totally surprised if it had been cultivated at all. Farmers are not good gardeners, I think mostly because they have not got the time and are possibly not over inclined to spend excessive hours tilling a few fancy flowers when they could be growing things for money just over the wall. In those busy years in the mid eighties I would use every available hour that I could to work in the Bureau office. Often, if after the early morning walk the children were still fast asleep, I would try and take advantage of the situation and start work early. I could always hear any awakenings on the baby intercom which had been wired through.

I used to advertise that the office was open from 6am onwards every day. Operating that way I found many farmers would telephone me before they started their full day's work. I suppose it was unusual then in the early 1980s to have an office up and running at this early time. Now of course people can telephone at any time of the day whilst doing anything, even on their tractors, with mobiles, so I don't offer the sunrise service anymore.

My Bureau office is in the old stables of the farm. All the buildings on the farm and around here in the Peak District of Derbyshire are of grey-white limestone with corners, window edges and door surrounds of honey coloured sandstone. They have the old sandstone roof tiles and of course all the limestone is beautifully weathered and mellow with a few creepers and patches of aged moss.

The stables are about a stone's throw from the farmhouse across our old farmyard. This is not the muddy, dung filled area that it would have been a hundred years ago but a clean, square tarmac expanse more like a modern day small car park. The farmyard is made up of buildings on three sides. One side is the farmhouse, one an old traditional barn and the third side is the old stables. They were used to house poultry for many years after the horses disappeared but were always referred to as the stables. Not long after I started the Bureau I realised that this would be the perfect place to have my office. In the transformation we only used half the stables and kept as much of the character of the place as possible. Three different rooms were made and the old wooden beams were left exposed in the ceiling. The original stone makes up part of the walls as well.

The first room you walk into is where I interview clients. I have two snug and cosy high backed velvet armchairs in a deep warm rose colour with a pretty country looking settee with matching curtains. Four of the plain cream walls now have masses of photographs of successful introductions. There are also two tables set against the walls, covered with smaller gold frames, containing wedding photographs.

I also have an old desk in this room where I take notes when I am talking to any clients who come to have an interview. Through the window I can look down through the farmyard to the front field and the farm drive.

The other two rooms are the true working rooms where the office equipment lives containing hundreds of profiles, maps and the paraphernalia needed to do the matching. I have always considered these offices my little domain, although of course they are usually shared with a secretary or two. It is where I have always loved to come to have time to myself.

Seeing me sitting in the office I suppose I must look like a stereotyped homely, comfortable and, I hope, friendly farmer's wife. I am still that rounded person I was as a little girl only now more so as the years have advanced. A bit like Dawn French, so I am told. I follow my whole family in being short, no more than five feet one inch and have a circular face with a rosy complexion. My blond curls of yesteryear have been replaced with brown mid length hair still naturally curly and always wispy and windswept, making me look as if I've been dragged through the proverbial hedge backwards.

I have to admit I am not the timid and shy person of my childhood days. I will approach anyone and say anything which I think needs saying. I have a serious, compassionate side to my personality but I certainly laugh a great deal and take a very optimistic and light hearted approach to life. I delight in seeing the funny side of everything we all do but I have to admit that I'm a bit thick at understanding jokes, so John tells me. Usually I have to have a joke explained twice to me.

I am accused by my friends of being slightly eccentric. I don't understand this at all but they seem so adamant that I am. I suppose I just do what I feel is right at the time. It doesn't bother me if others do not follow, or agree with me. So, thinking again about Dawn French in 'The Vicar of Dibley' maybe I am a lot like her but I carry with me more than a hint of the character of the simple, eccentric and gullible verger, Alice, the vicar's best friend.

I tend to wear feminine, flowery and full skirted clothes and tops generally but on interview days when clients visit me I always wear something smart with heels and do the very best I can with my wayward hair. Little does anyone know when they meet this reasonably well dressed, proficient looking woman, that I've possibly been dressed in the most undesirable garb you can imagine earlier that day, whilst doing something on the farm.

On one silaging day in 1988 I got out my big, very muddy pram, which I kept just for pushing the children around the farm. Underneath on the wire tray I would put the men's snap for their lunch. I had two or three baskets and bags tied to the sides with tea and cups, cake etc. It was incredibly cold that summer day so I wore a very old overcoat that was totally threadbare but so warm. It was so ancient that all the buttons had come off and the only way to close it around you was with a series of complicated pieces of baler twine. All this was put over a quite presentable dress as I was expecting a client to come to the office for an interview in the afternoon. The whole ensemble was completed with the essential wellies, of course. I had planned that when I got back, the children would have their afternoon nap and Anne would baby sit over at the house whilst I interviewed the client. Well, the snap had been taken up into the first field and as I was turning round the corner returning into the farmyard I caught sight of the client. He'd arrived early! He was alighting from the biggest and poshest Mercedes I had ever seen and was dressed in an immaculate suit with matching tie and pocket handkerchief. I think he was the smartest person to arrive in our yard, ever. I ducked back; he could not possibly see me like I was. You couldn't have told the difference between me and any good bag woman on the Embankment that afternoon.

Once he had been invited inside the office by Anne I tried desperately to get my overcoat off but I could not undo, come what may, the dreaded baler twine - I was like a trussed up chicken trying to extricate myself from this massive coat. I realised I had to get to the house and cut the strings with a knife but the only way I could pass the office to get to the house without him seeing me was to duck as low or even lower than the pram and push it past the office windows. I was like a demented wobbling duck that had picked up a bag lady's effects. I could see that Anne was keeping him talking with his back to the window but then he turned quickly and Anne said his face was a picture of absolute amazement as he caught sight of the pram with two laughing children travelling under its own steam past the office window. Thank goodness he did not take a closer look to see me, head down, knees apart, swaying slowly along hanging onto the underneath of the pram handle like a waddling, demented duck.

A quick slit of the ropes, kicking off of the wellies and a brush of the hair brought me to being the presentable, professional lady he had come to meet. Anne took over the children in the house and I settled into conducting his interview for the afternoon with complete aplomb.

It turned out that he had a large farm in Cheshire and his mother had sent him to me. She had obviously had a great influence on him because he promptly brought out a list of the all the qualities that she wanted him to find in his future wife. Mother had written down ten points which, without any deviation whatsoever, needed to be present in a future daughter-in-law. I asked him if he really wanted to find a special person to share his life with, honestly and truthfully, without his mother being there. Well no, he was quite happy, as he was. It was just that she wanted grandchildren so much. I'm afraid I had to send him on his way with a pep talk about having the courage to tell her exactly what he wanted in life.

On one of those early summer mornings a few years later I started to read through a registration form from Andy who lived on the Cumbrian moors. As he was not a dairy farmer I assumed he would not be an early riser and left my call to him until a little later.

I telephoned him and thanked him for his registration form and asked, really just as a matter of making conversation and learning a little more about him, why after being alone for so long he had just decided to try to meet a partner.

"Something just clicked in my head one day," he said. A broad Cumbrian accent trailed over the phone and I visualized a 'salt of the earth' man with maybe quite old fashioned clothes and with a few days stubble, as I knew he had lived alone for so long without any female influence.

"What do you mean?" I enquired.

In a slow, thick voice he described how on his forty ninth birthday, exactly twenty years to the day since he came to his farm, he decided that he was not going to continue with his life as it was. He was not melancholy in his conversation with me. In fact he was quite hearty and jolly, cracking a joke mostly at his own expense at what his mates would say if they knew he wanted a woman. He would never live it down and he'd have his leg pulled constantly.

So often of course this, 'I shouldn't really be doing this' attitude covers acute embarrassment or desperate shyness. I think with Andy it was total and absolute embarrassment. He was facing the fact that his lack of feminine company was important to him. In that macho world that so many men inhabit, their friends and workmates can control so much of their lives. Unknowingly they condemn someone to being completely lonely through their joking and boasts of 'who needs a woman.'

He said he would like to come for an interview at the office and so I said we needed to make an appointment for when he was going to come down.

"Well, it'll have to be in September when I come down for Hartington sheep sales," he replied.

The village of Hartington is about three miles from us and once a year they have well known sales with people attending from all over the country. He said he came to the sheep sales every year and he'd looked me up on the map and realised I did not live too far away. So I asked him to give me a call when he knew exactly when he was coming down and put his form aside. I was confident I would see him in September, when he would combine the business of trading sheep with finding a wife.

As I filed Andy's paperwork, I noticed John, outside my window. He was smiling and gesturing to me. He looked happy enough. I thought John, like me, had changed over the years. He was still broad and masculine in build but he had certainly thickened in his middle section. His glasses now gave him quite an air of authority, especially when he looked over them at anyone. For ten years John has sat as a magistrate on the local bench. He's always enjoyed getting away from the farm for a day and using parts of his brain that are not otherwise exercised in the normal course of farming. I'm told that one look over his glasses, when he is chairing a court, and about to pronounce a sentence, will convince any dangerous driver that the death penalty has been resurrected just for him. Otherwise he actually does still have a great, friendly smile, and his bushy beard that drew me to him so many years ago is still as full and as splendid as ever, but now flecked with grey maturity. His familiar figure, dressed as usual in green, check, country type work clothes seemed to be trying to tell me something as he gestured through the office window.

I looked again down the field and saw an army of tractors and machinery coming up the lane leading to the farm. All in a convoy like a green disjointed caterpillar possibly a quarter of a mile in length, they rolled up the drive and parked themselves up on the front field. No wonder John was happy. The silaging team had arrived.

Silage has taken over from hay on most of the farms in Britain. Hay making still takes place but to a very minor degree compared to years ago. The advantage of silage is that it can be harvested more quickly than hay. You don't have all that tedding and turning for days on end only to be rained upon with the result that you have to start all over again. Silage does not need particularly sunny or good weather when it is cut and it can be handled and stored very efficiently. Most of all it has a better nutritional content than hay and is therefore highly beneficial, particularly for dairy cows. Sadly, it smells different from the glorious waft of newly made hay but you just have to accept that old methods have gone and new ways of farming have taken their place.

Yes, the silage contractors had arrived and I knew full well that word would get around the farm instantly as everyone would have heard the noise as they approached. Quite quickly our farm workers seemed to have left whatever they were doing to come to the front field and walk around all the appliances and equipment and calculate how much everything had cost. Every year they announce how much more wealthy the contractors are. Of course the contractors, on hearing these announcements, always deny this totally and utter replies of complete disbelief, claiming that they are not a penny wealthier but certainly half a million more in debt!

Some farmers buy their own silage equipment and do it themselves but more and more employ contractors. They do actually come every year with more huge and efficient equipment and the job always seems to take less time. It used to take six to seven and sometimes eight days to cut and gather it all but with their newer and larger systems it seems now to only take two days to complete our usual two hundred acre harvest.

It's exciting when the contractors arrive as our usual routines are disturbed and there are fresh people for all to talk to with news to catch up on. It can be stressful for John though, as he wants his silage in quickly. But if all is straightforward and the weather is kind, then it's a good and happy time.

Our contractors have been visiting us for about eighteen years. Usually nothing except a breakdown stops them from working from early morning until it goes dark at night. They never stop except for ten minutes for their snapbox or when I take out supper.

That morning, just as all the men were gathered around the newly arrived machinery, Lynda arrived. Lynda had been working for me for eighteen months and was ravishingly attractive. The sway of her hips and her swishing long hair stopped every man in his tracks. They stared mesmerised as this gorgeous creature swept across the farmyard. And then came the comments. "Got a new woman for me, Lynda?" "Are you on the books love?" "I think I'll part exchange the wife."

There was one day we shall not forget easily. John and the farm workers were concreting a small portion of the farmyard as Lynda alighted from her car. All eyes were diverted to her petite and alluring figure. The concrete went everywhere but where it should have gone. There followed a lot of clearing up and explanations as to how it had happened had to be composed.

Lynda had come across all such comments before and took it all in her stride with a laugh and a joke. Unknown to the men, she had always brought a quality of toughness into my office. You would not, for a moment, realise that this beautiful and desirable woman was my mainstay when it came to getting in money that I was owed. Of course she had the other attributes that I appreciate: Quick typing skills and an understanding of country life as she was brought up in quite a remote Peak District village and had married a local farmer's son. Most importantly, though, she could cut a person dead on the phone with her expertise at getting them to pay their bills. No-one would realise when they looked at her long chestnut hair, angelic face and petite figure, that I valued her for her ruthlessness. The problem that I've always had is that I'm an old softie and would always be taken in by a sob story. Lynda would not.

The routine went on in the office that day. "Well, what do we have here? " I said aloud to myself. I smiled as I read through Jane's details. She had written that she wanted to meet a gentleman farmer. He must not work but have enough leisure time to take her out whenever she wished, and her main aim in life was to be able to organise his hunt balls! He should be tall, dark, handsome, very romantic, wealthy with a large country house and be preferably the Master of Foxhounds. It seemed to me she wanted a cross between the simmering passions of Darcy accompanied with his baronial country estate, the good looks of a young Nigel Havers and the social and hunting connections of Prince Charles.

For a moment I dreamily contemplated my own luck were I to meet such a man, tall and handsome, who rode out on his horse from his grand manor house daydreaming of meeting a dumpy, plump, pink, round faced middle aged lady like me. Then with all the brooding passion of Darcy he would pick me up as if I weighed no more than a feather and carry me away on his white charger for hours of rapturous lovemaking by the side of his shimmering lake.

Then I realised I'd got to get back down to the realms of reality. I thought about how I could gently let Jane into the secrets of the facts of this world. There again, Pat, I said to myself, never pre-judge and assume she is a plain Jane. She could have the body of Liz Hurley, the connections of Camilla and the sexual expertise of Madonna. How wealthy she was I suppose would not matter if she fulfilled all men's dreams with these combined attributes. I telephoned her and carefully went through the delicate tip-toeing sequence of finding out about her real situation in life. I started by explaining that gentlemen farmers hardly existed nowadays and if a glut of them did happen to live close by her luck would really be in. It seemed her connection with the countryside was that she had been brought up on a very small farm as a child. Her marriage had broken down, and she had been left with three children, all just going into their teenage years. Her only income was the maintenance cheque from their father. "When the kids are driving me mad I switch off from them and fantasize about my dream man," she told me. We came to an understanding after a long and difficult discussion that she would leave the choice of her introductions in my hands, but sadly the Master of Foxhounds never did turn up for her.

As I walked over from the office to the farmhouse I remembered I had to get supper for about twelve hungry men. Before I began I made myself a cup of tea to relax a little after the day's work and think about what I had in the pantry. As with most farm houses the pantry has always been as big as any normal room, and the old stone slabs to keep the food cool are still there.

The farmhouse is possibly about two hundred years old. Not very ancient when you consider many of the farmhouses in the locality would be twice that age.

It is detached from any of the other buildings around the yard and is situated on one side of the central farmyard. It looks like a very typical Derbyshire cottage in that it is double fronted with a central front door elevated slightly from the yard at the top of several old stone steps. Shrubs decorate the underneath of the windows on each side of the door. Years ago when the cows would have trailed through the farmyard to be milked in the shed, you could never grow pretty flowers in their pathway as they would have been immediately devoured as they sauntered to their milking appointment. However, times have changed and farm animals do not seem to roam anywhere and everywhere now.

Mere Farm was so called because up until the late 1950s it had no mains water at all and all the water for the stock came from large man-made ponds called meres, located around the farm. Meres are completely round and drop quickly to about six feet in depth. They are lined with clay and for centuries were the only source of water on the high limestone farms that are situated away from the rivers in the valleys. The main mere for the farm was directly at the back of the farmhouse, virtually lapping at the door of the old dairy. It was filled in and is now a circle of concrete with a complete round border of pretty flowering shrubbery. The children loved riding their bikes around and around this when young. We do still have several other meres around the fields which act as water sources for the cattle but everywhere also has mains water supplied.

Even on hot summer days my navy blue Rayburn is still rumbling on, so I went and put a joint of meat in it to cook slowly over the next two to three hours. The kitchen is quite long and has a section for sitting in comfy armchairs with newspapers constantly strewn about. There is a big central pine kitchen table which has chairs around for six, but several more chairs are lodged beside other walls for visitors' use. John always uses the chair that his father left him at the top of the table and I always use the small Windsor chair his mother gave me when we married.

Around the Rayburn at the top end of the kitchen are the work units. This is the hub of the kitchen. Black beams make up most of the ceiling which is not at all uniform. Two of the walls are made of exposed limestone. It is not a picture book, glossy magazine type farmhouse kitchen but a very liveable, warm and functional hub of our home.

The back entrance leads into a room that houses all the wellingtons, boots and shoes, seemingly sufficient for the population of our local town. There are coats for every season, sticks, flea sprays, sheep marking sprays and odd implements that would confound any mind as to what their function is. I guarantee you could make anything from the collection of bits and bobs you will find in this repository. You name it and it's there. Leading off from the back entrance is a room where all the men wash their hands on coming into the house.

I ferret away, finding jars of chutney, pickles, cakes, anything and everything that hungry men will eat in several hours time and start putting all this into large wicker shopping baskets to load easily into the back of the truck. At last I find my old huge teapot in the pantry that will provide gallons of tea to all and sundry. It's rested for several years next to a brand new sparkling tea urn that I refuse to use. It was my Christmas present from John one year. "An urn?" I exclaimed. "How can anyone with an ounce of romance buy his wife a tea urn for Christmas?" A hurt expression came over him. "But I thought you would like it," he said, totally disbelieving that I could long for anything more appealing.

When I went to pick the children up from the school bus I called into the village shop for the bread. I make a lot of sandwiches and put them with sausage rolls, pasties and other filling foods. I take tea, coffee and cider to drink and put all of them in the back of the pick-up. All the men stop at the same time and get together to eat. They always joke with our three farm workers and Ben and Sarah show off their skills driving the quad bike with the dogs following. It seems I am feeding the five thousand when in fact it's only about a dozen.

Tom, the boss man, usually gets off his tractor first and presents himself at the back of the Toyota pick up for supper. Then, as his workmen see this, I suppose they feel they can then do the same. It is great that they have been coming so long for you feel such old friends and can immediately go straight back into the conversation of last year, where you left off. Jo is the oldest man in the team and starts to get on at Tom. Tongue firmly in cheek he says he's not pulling his weight. I suppose he can say anything to Tom, knowing full well he can get away with it after the years of work he has given him. There seem to be some suggestions by one and all that Tom is surreptitiously going behind the wood for a sleep. I suppose any busy contractor working virtually day and night in the peak of the summer would give anything to have a sly sleep. But he just can't. Jo puffs on his pipe and takes great pleasure in stirring up matters. He then tells me about the latest child that he and his wife have fostered over the year.

By this time Tim has arrived. He is the buck raker or man that deals with all the grass once it has been brought to the silage pit. Tim is a quiet and rather serious man but lovely to talk to and a good worker. Keith appears and munches on the beef sandwiches and says he was starving. His machine picks up and chops the silage and he is so very particular about his straight and exact lines. Big beefy Brian eventually joins us. He will have been mowing a few fields away and always appreciates the food and says so. Others appear who are doing the carting and with our own men and John and the children you can have up to thirteen or fourteen individuals standing, sitting on the grass, drinking and eating around the truck.

We've enjoyed these picnics in blistering hot weather. At other times it has been so cold and windy it seemed more like January and I have produced a huge pot of stew or even gone to the local fish and chip shop to feed everybody. Usually it is just nicely warm and by coincidence the feeding stop is mostly in some of the picturesque parts of the farm with glorious views over the surrounding landscape.

When the silage team have moved off to another field I always try to go over to one of my favourite spots on the farm and sit in front of a nice, good little wood. (I wonder if other people find some woods sinister and eerie and some good and kind and peaceful to be in). This wood is always nice and comfortable. Over on the western boundary of the farm is Arbor Low, a pre-historic stone circle where people would have been burying their clan folk about five thousand years ago. Directly in front of me to the south was the old Roman road that led from Buxton into the southern lands. How many soldiers would have marched along there? To the left there are undulating and pock marked fields where lead mining took place about two hundred years ago. How strange that in this very isolated spot one thousand,three hundred feet above sea level, life has continued for generation, upon generation, and the lives of the people throughout that five thousand years have been so diverse and different. I always feel dwarfed by the immensity of the human experience in this enchanted location.

4.
The Perfect Match

As each year passes I find more and more people initially get in touch because they have been encouraged to do so by friends who have either had success with me or know someone else who has. This is great because straight away they have a positive attitude towards the Bureau as they know it can work.

But mostly people still get in touch through seeing my advertisements in farming and country newspapers, magazines or my web site.

Occasionally someone will telephone who married through the Farmers and Country Bureau several years ago but the marriage has now broken down. This is a very sad situation. But I suppose if one third of marriages end in divorce, some of my alliances will also eventually break down.

Sam from Devon married through me about eight years ago. When he telephoned recently I immediately sent my memory back over the years and located him in my mind, which enabled me to inquire after his wife. "Liz and I divorced a few months ago," he answered. "Things became difficult when her son from a previous marriage started to get older and my agricultural employment agency got busier. But we did have five good years together and I'd like to try again if you'll have me."

In some ways I always feel pleased when they re-visit me. Not pleased of course that they have gone through the trauma of divorce but that they do not feel it is my fault and that they still feel I can help them again.

The other quite new way that some people have got to know about the introduction agency in recent times is through advertising in doctor's surgeries. This is of course only in some of the very rural and isolated parts of the country. I suppose doctors in rural practices now realise that a contributory factor towards physical and mental illness is loneliness. Recognising this practice administrators have requested small posters to put up in the waiting room and brochures that can be handed to anyone who they feel would benefit from contacting me.

Tony, a man living in Northumberland, contacted me through a recommendation by his GP in 2000. We talked on the telephone and he told me about his depression. Through our discussions he decided to come to the office for an interview. I was so pleased about this. I didn't feel I could go ahead and accept his membership if I had not met him, as I was concerned that his depression was too advanced. When he attended the interview I learnt that his wife had died three years previously of breast cancer. He had a close and loving family but as the children had grown older, each year after the tragic event, another son or daughter would leave home for university or to progress their career. His depression got worse and worse in that he could not stand the thought of eventually being completely alone. He cried in my office as he told me about the last few years of his life.

I said I would not let him meet anyone for about three months. I asked him to try to get himself on an even keel and get stronger mentally before I gave him his first introduction. I told him that in his case I was aiming not towards a serious relationship to begin with as I do for most people. I felt it was important for him to just get out and start meeting new people, to enjoy new friendships, to visit new places and to generally develop a new life for himself in the company of others. Tony agreed to try to get the better of his depression and his last words on going out of the office door were, "I feel better already because you're giving me hope."

Tony and the first lady I introduced him to went out several times. He told me he enjoyed the looking forward to going out for the evening as much as the actual going out. He even joked with me on the phone about how he felt like a youth again, getting ready for a date, dressing up and wondering what she would be like.

Janet was the second lady he met and he started to really enjoy her company. She had never been married and was in her late forties. She was a career woman from Newcastle upon Tyne but she had always lived in the countryside. She told me how much she enjoyed the company of his children. They were not constantly at home, but they seemed to accept her in their father's life and she loved the family atmosphere. She also told me how different she was from his late wife and possibly this had got them off to a good start. She was not domesticated like his wife had been. She arrived at the farmhouse one day and Tony was making jam. "I wouldn't have a clue where to start," she told me. His wife had done all the farm paper work and the house work and was not an outside person. Janet, on the other hand, loved being involved in the physical aspects of farm work. On her days off from her work, she enjoyed driving a tractor or helping with stock. It was good that his wife and Janet could not really be compared. After about a year of going out I was informed that they were planning their life together and Tony said, "I've never looked back or had really bad depression since I met Janet."

Sometimes people like Tony are not actually ready for an introduction, although they feel they are. Possibly they have recently gone through a trauma in their life. Often their previous partner has left them or they are widowed and they just cannot bear the thought of being alone in the immediate future. They feel the solution is to join an introduction agency, quickly. In some ways it is only because that previous marriage or relationship was so good that they cannot bear not being part of a couple and want to quickly replace what they have lost. I have to talk to them in a sympathetic and understanding manner but I explain that they will never recapture what has now gone. Only when they have faced up to this and looked on their next relationship with fresh eyes are they ready to continue with meeting more people.

The very common opening line when anyone telephones me is "I've never done anything like this before." Twenty years ago people were far more embarrassed to join an agency than they are now. It is definitely becoming more acceptable to meet others through this medium. We would all like to casually and naturally meet someone special, fall madly in love and live happily ever after without the involvement of a third party. But, sadly, that perfect world is not enjoyed by everyone.

When people request a brochure over the telephone, you can get the person who is very business-like and orders the brochure as they would a travel catalogue without any chattiness. Then you get the other extreme. People who give you their life history in the first two minutes and they want to know everything about the agency instantly. I've had parents requesting brochures for their sons and daughters (usually mothers), bosses asking for the brochure to be sent to their employees and daughters asking on behalf of their mothers or fathers. Sometimes I will get a brochure sent back to me in the post with words such as, "I don't need this" written across it. I assume it has been requested by some friend or relative thinking that they know what is best, but obviously do not.

Some people come to the office to see me for an interview. I feel I cannot force people into a face to face interview because, of course, many join from hundreds of miles away. It is very difficult to drop everything and travel to see me and I do realise that some people seem to find the prospect of sitting in front of me for two hours or more totally daunting. I do feel I make the interview a pleasant and rewarding experience but of course people have pre-conceived ideas.

I must admit I love doing these interviews and I cannot believe my luck that I can regularly get to know a complete stranger on a one to one basis. Many people say they have never before been able to talk about themselves completely for such a long time. Issues are discussed that may relate to future dates or relationships.

One of the most important questions I ask is to describe what they would like their life to be like in three years time if they met someone special. This is very revealing and really does help me in getting to know that new member. Although the past can be important and the present certainly is, to put two people together who are looking for the same in life, the future is vital.

I give advice where I can see it is needed or requested. Simple questions to some can be the hardest to overcome. What do I wear? Where do we go? How do I behave? What do I do? and a hundred other queries. I always talk about all these as sensitively and thoroughly as I can and of course everything is completely confidential.

One day I was expecting a client whose mother had telephoned and made an appointment. I heard a car come into the farmyard and as I looked out of the window I saw the driver lean over and open the passenger door and give an almighty push making the young man on the passenger side practically fall out of the car. He was looking quite stunned as he stood there on the tarmac while his driver sped away. I went out to him and he seemed to have no idea where he was.

After I'd introduced myself, he said "I never thought she would go to such lengths to get me here." He was my next interview but obviously it was through the instigation of his mother and not because he wanted to come. I took him into the office and gave him a cup of tea and when he had calmed down I told him that he must stand up to his mother. If he was not interested in finding a partner, then that was his decision in life and he must tell her that. His mother quietly drove back into the yard after about an hour and I left him to confront her.

On another day I had back to back appointments. I had just cleared my desk and was reading through the notes on my next client, when there was a tap at the window and there stood a cyclist just taking off his bicycle clips from his tweedy trousers. He was also wearing a flat cap and a checked shirt. 'Now what?' I thought, 'Not another lost tourist.' In the event it turned out to be my next interview appointment. He had no car and his brother needed the farm vehicle to take some stock into market so he had decided to cycle from West Yorkshire to keep the interview appointment. "My God, it's a long way," he cried as he got his jacket out of his carrier on the bike. Once he'd put that on you would never have know that he'd just cycled that incredible distance. I was in awe at such dedication to see me.

I do at times get very shy men and women but usually it is the men who are the more apprehensive. They describe how they would just die at the thought of talking to a woman they did not know in a romantic fashion on the phone. One man had a very pronounced stutter. So I suggested he wrote to her. I tell men that most women would be delighted to receive a letter from a man as this lovely way of communication is not commonly used nowadays.

I remember I had great difficulty with one man as he felt he could not make the initial contact by phone as he was so shy and he could not easily put pen to paper. I told him that I would help him write letters as long as when he eventually met the girl he would tell her the truth immediately. He told me what he wanted to say and I wrote the letters for him. After about three months the crunch time came when they had to meet. I was so nervous for him as I'd really got to know and like this man whilst helping him write his letters. Amazingly all went really well and they quickly decided to tell everyone that they had met at their local vets. Actually all must have gone very well indeed because they are now happily married and have two children.

Sometimes it is better to not take someone on or fill them with false hope when they will be eventually disappointed. This is when you know full well it is going to be very difficult to match them with someone. This rejection can be because they live in a difficult area or are a difficult age. It's a very fine line because at other times you can judge, after speaking to a person on the phone, that the thing they want most is hope and that they will meet a partner. So sometimes, even if I think their chances of meeting someone through me are slim, I don't return their registration forms but say I will keep their details just in case someone comes along. I do not actually register them and of course I return their payment. In this way I am under no obligation to give an introductory service, which would be very difficult to do if this person is so hard to match. It does, however, keep hope alive.

Once a person says they wish to join the Bureau a profile is completed. This is a description of that person from what they have said about themselves in their registration form. Then the matching process begins.

Of course before you go into the finer points of matchmaking you have to get the basic factors right first. Considerations such as area and age, then you can look at their smoking habits, marital status, religion, children they might have, or wish to have, educational background, personality and compatible aspects of the countryside. When I've got about three or four potential matches using these basic points I will then consider the finer points such as a liking or not of pets, horses, blood sports, holidays preferred, politics, interests and hobbies. The individual preferences that you personally know about people through interviewing them or talking at length with them on the phone are considered and then, last but not least, their hopes for the future and the type of lifestyle they wish to lead. Do they want to change career? Move to another part of the country? Expand their farming business? Be part of a family? There are so many aspects to think about. Often, there is a very obvious match that stands out from the rest when you have thought about everything.

When I have decided on the particular match letters are sent to both people with profiles, and they are asked to reply either by returning the letter or telephoning the office to indicate if they wish to go ahead or not. Of course most people telephone in as they really like to talk to me about the prospective introduction. "Do you know any more?" they ask which invariably I do not as I put all that I can disclose in the profile.

With a 'Yes' from both parties, each person's first name and telephone number are sent out to their prospective match on the same day and the gentleman is asked to make the initial contact. The lady will be expecting a call and with these preliminary obstacles well and truly overcome you hope all will go well.

To report back on whether introductions were a success or not some clients write back to the office with reams of explanations on how it all went. Some give the briefest of explanations such as just the word "good" or "no good." Others call in and you get a complete run down on the confusion with the cars. So many times I've been told over the years of couples planning to meet at a pub not knowing that it had two car parks. One car would wait in the one park and the second car in the other. Thinking that their 'introduction' had not turned up they would go home, destined never to meet.

I've been told of men forgetting their wallets and fumbling about in the car to find an odd pound or two so that when they walk with her into the pub they can at least buy a drink. Sometimes ladies get totally lost driving to a location and I've had distress calls of 'I'm completely lost, help!' One gentleman from the Channel Islands would fly his own helicopter to the designated meeting place and pick the lady up to fly on to wherever she wished to go. I've had train spotters take a lady out for the day 'spotting trains' thinking the date would take great delight in that activity. "Never, never, never again," has been shouted down the phone line.

Then of course I've heard from ladies who have been told 'I've just got to nip back to see a calving cow' only to spend the rest of the evening ankle deep in a cold muddy field bringing forth new life.

One lady, a school teacher in her early thirties, planned to meet up for the first time during half term. "So it doesn't matter about getting back home too early, "she said. When they met, they were instantly, completely and absolutely besotted with each other. She decided to return back to his farm that evening and whatever came to pass made her decide not to return home for a week. I am pleased to say they married at the next end of term holidays.

I've had people telephone me from the pub toilets to say, "He's awful, how do I tell him I don't want to see him again." I tell them to say, "It's been so nice to spend the evening with you, I'm really pleased we met but I don't think we're suited to a long term relationship." This is why I stress that you should not give anyone your full name and address until you are sure you want to go ahead and see them on a regular basis. So often, even if you know you are not totally compatible together, it can be nice to remain friends.

Of course no matter how many photos you see of another person you can't tell how you will feel until you are in their company, facing them, talking and standing close to them. Is there a spark, a curiosity to know them better, a warmth between you, an inclination of being truly interested in you. People so often expect the bells to ring and 'the earth to shake' and unless this happens they think this person is not 'the one'. It can happen like this but many times it can gradually occur over a period of time. I've heard so many times from people that when they first met their partner they thought that never in a million years could they ever marry this person. They felt no strong compatibility but mostly they felt no spark, no wish to be physically close to them. With the second meeting, amazingly, everything felt different. It might have been because both were less apprehensive and more relaxed. Their true selves were revealed or because they had got to know and appreciate each other better. But they looked at each other in a different way and suddenly realised what a nice interesting person they were with.

If only I could sprinkle on all my clients that magical component that makes them fall in love. That really is all most of us want; to find that special person and live happily ever after.

5.
Go Forth and Multiply

S ometimes, as I sit in the office and pin forms together, I ask myself if it is my skill in actually joining these two people together or has everyone got a destiny all set out for them.

When I first read through a new registration form I try to understand the specific written picture of that person. It is easy to put everyone into a known category; 'The workaholic farmer,' 'The horsey woman,' 'The would be country gent,' 'The village odd job man,' 'The doggie lady,' 'The greenie,' 'The typical farmer's daughter.' But no one is the same or wholly what you think.

Another exercise I do, of course, when reading a new form is to assess how easy or how difficult I feel it will be to find a partner for them. I've had women who would be very difficult to match up. In fact I've nearly said to them, "Sorry I cannot help you," just to have fate tell me that I don't know everything, for, to my complete and absolute amazement, they have found success on their first introduction.

There are some basic factors I will look for when thinking about difficulties such as a short man or a tall lady. If you are a man under five feet eight inches your chances are radically reduced as ladies so often want to meet tall men. There seems to be a higher percentage of men who will meet a taller lady than ladies who will meet a shorter man. I always get more men than ladies who wish to join the introduction agency up until about thirty four years old. Then the ages seem to level off reasonably well. Once you get into the middle forties far more ladies approach to join, as there are so many unattached ladies in their forties and fifties. Maybe it is because if a marriage ends when the couple are heading towards fifty it is so often because the man has actually found a younger woman. This sadly leaves the older wife alone. Of course where my Bureau is concerned the greater connection a woman has with the countryside or farming, the more quickly she'll get snapped up.

Older men so often feel they do not need anyone to help them find a partner. They can do it by themselves, they say. In reality they sometimes can, but so often farmers and country men do not meet the right woman.

A high percentage of my first introductions are successful and the clients never come back onto the register, but to achieve that you've got to come up with someone the likes of whom they have not met for years in their own lives. We may call this luck but is luck the final result of the destiny that was meant to be for you anyway?

There was only one time when I was absolutely positive that the two people I put together would actually marry, and I think I would have taken a bet on it, I was so confident. Edward had joined my Bureau about a month before and, unusually, I had interviewed him at his home in Oxfordshire. When Elizabeth came to the office for her interview, she had only been with me for ten minutes and I said "I know who I am going to introduce you to, and I think you will be married within a year."

"But you can't say that, how on earth can you say that," she said. I agreed with her it was a ridiculous statement to make, but I felt so strongly that it would be the case.

About nine months later I had a stand at the Royal Show. Edward and Elizabeth came to see me on the showground and told me of their forthcoming marriage. I must admit I did then feel that destiny had taken a hand with them. About four years ago they brought their three lovely blond haired children to visit me at the farm.

But the path of true love doesn't always run smoothly. September arrived and Andy from Cumbria telephoned me to say he would be at Hartington sheep sales in a few days time and, as he had mentioned in his conversation with me in the summer, he wanted to come for an interview. The picturesque village of Hartington, about three miles away from us, is renowned for its village pond, the cheese factory making Derbyshire Stilton and for the annual sheep sales.

"I don't know what time I'll get to you. It depends on what I sell," said Andy on the phone two days before coming down. "I'm bringing down a lorry full of sheep."

I looked through the Bureau office windows many times when I suspected I'd heard a lorry coming down the drive but he must have been delayed.

As I was totally immersed in some introductions, I jumped a mile at a knock on the office window. No-one had driven down the drive so I didn't think I'd got a visitor, but yes I had. A man was standing outside the window gesticulating that he wanted to come in. He introduced himself as Andy as he stepped through the door and took off his cap.

"Andy, how on earth did you get here? I didn't hear your lorry."

I was quite bewildered. It was as if he had been dropped from the sky. Where was his wagon?

"I left it at 'artington," he said. "I didn't want anyone to see me lorry coming down your drive. They might 'ave thought I was after a wife, so I've walked over t'fields, that way no one can see me."

I smiled to myself. Well this was a first. That someone had traversed the three miles of walls, valleys, moorland and woods between us and the sheep sales on foot, just in case, on this darkening evening, someone might happen to see his lorry turn up our drive, and just happen to know it when he must live at least two hundred miles away! This determination definitely warranted a successful match.

Andy was a tall man, over six feet in height, and had quite a mop of grey hair. It was very thick and bouncy and sort of stuck out from his head, horizontally, before and after he took off his cap. This cap was strategically placed on the side of his head at a very acute angle. He was broad and stocky, a bit weighty, with massive hands. He was in his market clothes, for him possibly the smartest he would wear year in year out with a green waistcoat, a tweedy jacket with working brown trousers and boots. I asked him to sit down and poured the usual cup of tea and asked him to tell me about himself.

"Oh! Bloody hell. Nobody's ever wanted to know about me."

"Well, I do," I said.

He took a deep sigh and began his story.

"Well, like I said to you before, I decided to do something about myself way back in June. When I got up one morning, I looked in the mirror and said, God it's been twenty years since I've been here."

I encouraged him to carry on. "Been where - what did you mean?" I asked.

"You see me wife and I moved onto our farm twenty years ago. I was twenty nine and she was twenty seven years old."

"Tell me more, Andy," I said, as he seemed to dry up a little. He constantly seemed to think that one sentence sufficed as a description of his whole life. "I really need to know a lot more about you," I urged.

"I couldn't believe it. One day she was there and the next she was gone. She had taken all her stuff. We'd only been married just coming up for three months. We moved in the week after we were married on 5th April, my birthday. I bought the place and took it over on Lady Day.

She told me she found the place was difficult to live in. Leading up to the wedding she knew I was going to buy the place and what the farm was like and that it was going to be hard work. I never really knew after that what the trouble was. She just left without telling me and I never saw her again. I found out she was all right because she would send her mother letters, but not to me, not once."

After a pause and much twisting of the cap in his hands, which he had kept resting on his knee, he said, "I don't ever talk much about this sort of stuff, you know."

"I can understand that," I replied, "But you need to tell me about the time straight after your wife left."

"Hell - it was just like hell. I just sat. I'd do what I had to do with me stock, but that's all. I suppose I just survived, but it was the shock of it all, you see. I just couldn't believe it. I've never talked about it to anyone like this in all those years. I keep myself to myself you see, to do with these sort of thoughts. My family were brought up to get over things, so I've never even talked to my mother, in all these years."
I told him it was best to try and talk about deep feelings so that he could put it all behind him and start afresh.

Gradually he went on.

"I'd known her many a year before. Then we started going out when I was about twenty five. Up until then I was too busy trying to get started by myself. Dad had a small farm, but I was determined I was going to get me own place. I started me own flock when I was seventeen and every year got a few more and rented more land. I've always been a dealer as well. It just came natural, like. When I saw the farm up for sale I knew straight away that I wanted it. I got together as much money as I could and applied for a mortgage. With all that in hand, it seemed only natural to ask her to marry me. It was a quick wedding but we'd known each other for years."

I then asked Andy if he had ever gone through a divorce. "Ah, yes," he said. "About five years after she left I had letters from a solicitor telling me she wanted a divorce. I just signed everything and it was all over. Best thing really."

All of a sudden I saw this large masculine man, confused and trying so hard to understand how all that he had described could happen to him. Since he had been alone he had devoted himself to making the farm successful. He had paid off the bank loan and had accumulated more acres and a large breeding flock of good sheep. His dealing had spread far and wide through Cumbria, Northumberland and the Pennines.

After a bit more conversation, I was pleased that he seemed to start to relax, and we agreed that I would start to look straight away for a suitable lady. After a couple of hours, he departed as he had come, silently and stealthily, like the Black Magic man in the dark of night from the television adverts.

I set to in the next week searching for an introduction for Andy. I thought she would have to be a down to earth woman, someone very familiar with farming. I came across Beth who lived in Yorkshire and sent Andy's details to her.

Beth very quickly phoned back and her comment was, "He's a bit too up market for me. All this hunting, shooting and fishing - he sounds like a country gent."

Just as I was about to explain that he was not like that at all, she said, "But my friends think I should have a go, no matter what, so I will."

The next day I had another interview in the office with a male client. Usually I never answer the office phone when I am doing an interview, but that afternoon my secretary was off sick, so I had to cope with both. It was Andy replying to the profile of Beth that I had sent him.

"I'm glad I've got hold of you. I'm stuck inside doing paperwork this afternoon because the job I was going to do needed my neighbour's help and the awkward bugger said he'd got to go out somewhere. Anyway, yes, I'll be introduced to her if she wants, but God, does it have to be a Yorkshire lass?

"What's wrong with Yorkshire?" I exclaimed.

"They always know their own minds, too well. I'm sorry, I suppose I just can't see this sort of thing working for me and I'm in a bad mood because Dick's had this day away and I hate paperwork."

I put the phone down, concealing a small wry smile, and returned my attention to Richard, who had been waiting patiently.

For a month there was complete silence from them both, and then one day Beth telephoned. I said how nice it was to hear from her and asked how things had gone with Andy.

"Well, I never really believed it would work. In fact, I thought it would be utterly hopeless. To be quite honest, I really didn't think anyone would be interested in me, but the thing is - we're getting on very well. We're very similar in our ways and each time he comes over to me, things get better between us. Of course each time he comes he brings his wagon and usually goes out and buys some sheep so he doesn't have an empty journey going back. But that's all right. Next time we meet I'm going over there. So we'll see how it is then."

'What a wonderful down to earth, practical and tolerant woman,' I thought to myself as I put down the phone.

As the weeks went by, the next one to telephone was Andy. "Eh, she's a cracker of a lass, she is." He then went silent and I sensed he wanted to talk, but could not quite get it out. Eventually he told me that Beth was going to stay the weekend at his house in a few days. I said that seemed a good sign and asked what he was worried about.

"It's been so long, you see," he said. "You know what I mean. It's been a long time, since I entertained a lady. What will she expect?"

I then realised that for a straight talking northern man to discuss 'entertaining' and all that it implied was getting a bit too much for him as he seemed to be huffing and puffing a bit by then.

"Andy, it's like riding a bike. Once learnt, never forgotten. It will all come back to you, mark my words."

A little time went by and Beth telephoned me again and started the conversation by explaining she had something really difficult to cope with, to do with Andy. Then she went on to say that she now knew why Andy's wife had left him. My mind raced on and I dreaded whatever I was going to hear next. Could it be a voracious sexual appetite? With a lump in my throat I said, "Why Beth?"

"It's that house! I've been to some run down places in my life. I've never seen anything like it before and Andy says it was just like it is now when they moved in on their honeymoon. There are no floor coverings anywhere, just stone and bare floorboards and there are floorboards missing all over the place. The windows are open to the rain and wind and wallpaper just hangs off the walls. No wonder his wife left him! I put my foot down and refused to visit him again if I have to enter that house. So he's said he'll buy a caravan and we can do our courting there. The thing is that I get on with him so well. So I'm not going to let this damn house get the better of me."

Well Beth's practical nature did win in the end. Six months later she telephoned me to say the old house was being demolished and they were having a brand new house built which they would move into, together. She said that they had gone into it all and had got an architect to do the plans and that they had already been passed. The local planning board were so pleased that the eyesore Andy had called a house could be pulled down that they readily passed the plans.

"It'll be a wrench for me to completely leave my smallholding and friends in Yorkshire, but I love the man and I want to be with him. Anyway, I've put my place up for sale. There is no turning back."

When I'd complemented her on her success and told her he obviously just needed a woman like her I was so euphoric at that point, that I raised both hands in the air and shouted "Yes, I did it." It never varies. If I'm alone or with someone else in the office when I hear of another successful match I raise both hands as if in salutation of my great satisfaction in finding love and happiness for another couple. It is always the same. Both hands go up and I shout for joy.

I'm often invited to visit couples who have got together through the agency. These visits are very satisfying and happy occasions, and I like to make a short holiday for myself, perhaps visiting friends or family as well.

About a year after I'd heard from Beth, I was invited to visit Richard and Mary, who also lived in Cumbria, and Jessica and Hamish, a couple in Scotland who had telephoned and mysteriously said they had a very big surprise for me!

I came off the motorway and drove over the high fells of the Lake District. Richard had told me his farm was very isolated and the closest neighbour was about a mile away. When I arrived they both greeted me warmly and I sat down straight away to have a cup of tea and started to tell them about Jessica and Hamish who I was going to visit next. After about five minutes a knock came at the door and immediately Richard and Mary started giggling and smiling and announced that they also had a surprise for me!

To my absolute amazement, in walked Andy, the same Andy who had visited my farm with his cross-country SAS tactics about a year before. I looked at him open mouthed and managed to ask him what on earth he was doing here.

He edged into the room and there behind him, grinning broadly - everyone was grinning broadly - stood Beth.

"Well here's your surprise Pat" said Mary. "Andy and Beth are our next door neighbours! Andy and Richard have lived side by side here on the Cumbrian moors for twenty years!"

Mary went on to explain that she and Beth had got talking, and found out that Richard, Dick to his friends and Andy had both been members of my Bureau for many months. Next door neighbours who worked together most days and talked about everything under the sun, but never dreamt of telling each other that they were seeking partners through a marriage bureau.

It eventually sank in and they went on to tell me even more.

"Do you remember," Richard said, "That I came to your office for an interview? Well that day I was supposed to help Andy with some farm work, but I told him I'd got to go out for the day. I really came down to see you in Derbyshire."

Andy then followed on by reminding me that he'd been a bit annoyed that Dick had gone off for the day, but little did he know when he telephoned my office and I gave him Beth's telephone number, that Dick was actually sitting there by my side!

We all fell about with mirth and amazement at this coincidence and they were all for opening the whisky and making a party of it. But I still had to get to Scotland, so I had to refuse.

Beth and Andy insisted that I see their house before I left, though, so we cut across the field and there it was. It was really lovely and certainly no expense had been spared. You could tell another happy ending was in sight. They even looked alike. Country faces blooming with health; round, ruddy and extremely down to earth. An embarrassed smile covered Andy's face and I looked knowingly back at him and felt certain that his long-forgotten skills had come to the surface without too much difficulty.

But the day's surprises were not over.

I got into my car and resumed my journey north. I was heading for a hotel at Ballater, not far from Balmoral. Angela and I had been friends for many years and were rarely able to see each other, so occasionally we met up in a nice hotel where we could be pampered and catch up with all our news. Angela and I, (with our mutual friend Jenny) had been in deep trouble once with Matron, for joyriding in my little car, when we were student nurses. It seemed ironic that when we were all nursing she was the one constantly making the nursing blunders yet she had stayed in this career and had climbed the ladder in her profession. She had moved around the country, whilst advancing her career. This journey all worked in rather well because only about 50 miles away from Balmoral I intended to break my journey to visit Jessica and Hamish.

I knew they had been married for about two years. I'd not met either of them before but I thought this surprise they had in store for me very intriguing. It couldn't be another neighbour, could it?

When I arrived at their farmhouse it looked about a thousand years old. It was made of dark stone, maybe granite, and stood like a fortress as I approached it from the distance. It seemed enormous and was surrounded on three sides by high grassy slopes with huge farm buildings positioned to the back of the house. Jessica greeted me at the door and seemed so pleased that I had arrived virtually to the minute that she was expecting me.

"Oh! I'm so pleased you've arrived on time. Hamish has left combining to come down to meet you for a little while, before we have something to eat."

Hamish arrived almost immediately and, as I always do, I took a really close look at this couple. Jessica's most striking feature was her beauty. She had pale skin and black hair and I understood how Hamish could have fallen for this exquisite woman. He was broad and masculine with a full head of auburn hair and very blue eyes. They made an extremely attractive pair.

I started to ask about their lives before they met and Hamish described how he had never married. He had just not met anyone and really never stood a chance because he had always worked such long hours, always living on his remote farm and was quite shy. Jessica had lived all her life in a village about twelve miles away but had never known Hamish. She had been married before at a very early age, but they had grown apart, had not had children and had divorced in her mid-twenties.

"Life was rather dull then and really, for the next ten years, I did nothing with my life except work," she added.

Jessica told me how they decided to get married about six months after they had met. Some of her close family thought this was too soon but they could see no point in waiting as they were getting older and they wanted to be together and decided on a small white wedding at the local church.

They both then apologised for not being in touch since their wedding. Then they looked at each other and laughed and said how busy they'd been in the last year. "Anyway, come with us into the kitchen to see the surprise we have been keeping for you," said Hamish.

I followed them both into the farm kitchen. Hamish beckoned me to come to the far end of the room and my eyes moved to the right hand corner. I really could not take in what I was seeing. There before me were four babies, all about a year old, all playing together, laughing and smiling in a big wooden playpen.

"This is our surprise. This is what has kept us so busy over the last year.

These are our quads, all boys, born just over a year ago, "Jessica proudly announced.

I have to be honest in saying I think this was one of the biggest shocks I've ever really had in my entire life. I stood there staring in total disbelief. I uttered "Quads, quads, I'm responsible for quads, for quads!" and we all laughed together.

At last I recovered from the shock and began to ask them both if they had had fertility treatment. "Oh! No," Hamish proudly announced. Then Jessica coyly admitted that she knew the babies were soon on their way two or three months after they were married. One by one a cry, a shout, a noise and banging came from four individual babies and it was time for them and us to have our meal. Each was put in a high chair, and mum had one each side of her and dad had one each side of him. They were helping themselves very much to their own dinner but with continual help from mum and dad. I just could not keep my eyes off them all.

Hamish had to go straight out after the meal to continue with combining but he gave me a great big hug and some flowers and also a big photo of the babies all sitting together in a row. "When I joined your Bureau and you introduced me to Jessica, never did I imagine how my life would change. Somebody up there decided I'd had it too quiet for too long and said let's change his life completely. But thank you, Pat."

So for the next hour I helped give each one of those lovely little babies their afternoon bottle which they had before they settled down to a sleep. Jessica told me she did have help with them but today they wanted to manage alone to have privacy with me. They were all bundled into a massive big black pram that looked like a hundred years old with two at one end and two at the other. Jessica explained it was the farm pram that she allowed to get dirty but for going out to town they had specially adapted buggies that slotted together. She pushed the pram out and we walked around and then over to my car and I left Jessica standing by her big pram waving me goodbye with her four babies fast asleep.

When I returned home after a week, I immediately rushed up to John and said "You'll never believe what I've got to show you!" He didn't know anything about my journey up to Scotland as we do not usually speak to each other when I am away. I've always found it nicer to catch up on everything together when I get back. I produced the photo of the quads and said "What do you think of that? Just look what I'm responsible for. Isn't it wonderful? Four little babies, quads born to the farmer and his wife I visited in Scotland."

John looked at the photo in silent disbelief, shook his head sorrowfully, and said "Good God woman, do you realise what you've you done to the life of a poor unsuspecting bachelor?"

6.
What's for You Won't Go By You

Whether it is fate, luck or good business that brings people together, more often than not the first thing that attracts is appearance. You see someone and fancy them. Then, depending on the strength of the attraction, the boldness of the people involved and all sorts of other incidentals, words might be exchanged, meetings arranged, and there you are, suddenly in a relationship. But if people can't meet the right type of potential partners easily, perhaps because they are not living close by, how do they ever meet? There is no doubt that introduction agencies offer a unique and valuable service for many people, especially in these circumstances. They provide golden opportunities which would otherwise have been missed.

Instinct made me pair together the most unlikely man and woman, one a comedy actress from London, the other a sheep farmer from a remote Scottish island. This couple had to surmount all sorts of obstacles to have even their first meeting; different personalities, work commitments, parental wishes, not to mention a distance of five hundred miles between them! There were many false starts, hesitations and doubts along the way, but it was an exciting journey of discovery for them both. This is their story.

Mary had a successful career on the stage, TV and working as an agent for comedians in London, but she knew her career wasn't going to make her happy and she wanted to get out. She attended Quaker meetings and during the quietness of one of those meetings, she realized that the only thing that would make her happy would be to get married and have children. So she decided to set this course of action in motion. Her parents had a farm on the slopes of Snowdonia and she really wanted to go back there. All her friends knew she wanted to live in the country, and one in particular had done a television programme on my Bureau so she had some good background information. Mary decided to join up. She decided there was no reason to put all her eggs into one basket and she wasn't going to set her stall by it. It was just an interesting chance.

She told me, "There's nothing more disappointing than going out with someone for a few months, and then him saying something like, 'Oh of course, I can't stand children.' In normal circumstances you skirt round issues like that because you don't want to put people off. Quite often I found I was dating people with all sorts of hidden problems and unresolved issues. They didn't know what they wanted. I was becoming sure about what I wanted but was misplacing my trust in people and being hurt. So to sum it up, I wanted to get control of my life. I'd got control of my career and I'd got control of my health. I'd started becoming physically fit and I'd got control of my smoking a few years before so I asked myself, why can't I get control of my love life? Instead of waiting for somebody else, why don't I try this? It's been offered to me. You clearly weren't a rip-off which is a danger with dating agencies. You didn't charge an excessive amount and it seemed to me, having run a small business myself, that what you were charging was a fair covering of your costs plus a little profit. That was important to me, a clear indication that you were genuine. When I got your brochure, I thought, well this is somebody trying to do some good. There was no guarantee you were going to work magic, but there was no harm in trying. What is important about your agency is the fact that people who have joined it have come to you knowing what they want in life, and that's a huge step forward."

Fraser knew he wanted a wife and family. He'd had a relationship with a South African the previous year that didn't work out. Being on an island is tricky because a lot of the girls move off after school. So, unless you happen to find your partner early on, it's difficult to meet the right person. His father had been in the army and he was born in Germany. He lived there until the age of three when the family moved to Hampshire and then to Aviemore in the Highlands before they ended up on the Isle of Skye when he was seven. His mother was the farmer in their family, and it was the same with Mary, which is quite a strange coincidence. They both had a broadness of experience that was unusual in farming and both parents came to farming late in life compared to most people.

Fraser told me, "I suppose I had been thinking all winter that I wasn't getting any younger and opportunities weren't exactly landing on my doorstep. One evening my mother threw the Farmers Weekly at me open at the page advertising your Bureau - little did she know what she's started! I suppose she wanted me to marry and come back to the farm and retain the lifestyle. As it turned out, she was disappointed with the outcome, not imagining a wife would have her own farm. I suppose I was quite sceptical about applying to an introduction agency but I thought I had nothing to lose. It gets you out of the house and why not? I was quite excited about the idea of meeting someone. I thought it would be tricky to find anyone remotely near, and I knew it was going to be difficult to meet because of the way farming is. You can't just disappear and go here, there and everywhere, and money was a consideration because I didn't have any! No, it was obviously going to be difficult for me. I needed to be sure that we had enough in common before going to that effort."

I spoke on the phone for some time to Mary, and the phrase that kept coming back to me was 'intelligent sheep farmer.' She also said she didn't mind where she lived because she had to travel from London anyway. Fraser was also open-minded about who he met as long as he didn't have to waste time with women who would be totally unsuited to farming life on a remote island.

They both filled in the initial forms, giving the basic information I required. Mary commented on how strange it was to find out about people via that small piece of prose that I send out. She said she was impressed by Fraser's admission that he played the accordion, and in brackets "badly!" If somebody could joke about himself like that, she thought, he sounded like fun. Fraser said when he read Mary had been to university he decided she must have some brains, and the fact that she described herself as gentle, vivacious and with a good sense of humour definitely interested him. He added that when she said her first love was sheep farming, he felt this could be artistic licence.

They found out a lot about each other in the first letters. Mary was in an awkward situation where she was sharing a flat with a male friend, and without making a big thing about it, she didn't want Fraser to think she was involved with him. Her flatmate was gay. She emphasised that she was considering moving back to North Wales to her parents' farm at the end of the year. This move was for two reasons; one was that she was fed up with London and the other because she wanted to spend some time closer to her parents who were unwell. She liked her parents and wanted to get to know them better. She talked about her work. She had wanted to become an actress and ended up being an agent for comedians such as Michael Bentine and John Pertwee. In fact, the death of Willie Rushton, who was both a friend and client, was a trigger for her. She described her last meeting with him.

"He was one of the best people to work with and when he died, I thought, I've worked with the best now, I can't better that. Willie died undergoing routine heart surgery, and really the last time I saw him, he was hiding under his bed sheets at the hospital, and he said 'Oh, the curse of Mary.' I said, 'Don't be so ridiculous, it's only heart surgery. We've still got shows to do.' In fact he was laughing about the brochure you're given before the operation. It says that after recovery you can hang-glide and parachute and go rock climbing and he said 'Marvellous, I've never been able to do those things before. I'm really looking forward to it.' But he didn't pull through and it really knocked me for six. His death made me think, right, I've been messing about, thinking about moving, I'm going to set myself a year to leave, tidy up loose ends, sort my life out, get fit, and go back to North Wales. It felt like home although I hadn't grown up there. Spiritually, it felt like my home. And this was the same sort of time I was in touch with Fraser. Gradually things became clearer."

Mary's letters would be full of jokes and humour to cover her nervousness, whereas Fraser's were slightly more factual. Fraser remembered getting out the silver letter opener to open Mary's first letter and thinking, "Well, is this it? Is this the person I'll marry?" Mary admitted to not knowing where the Isle of Skye was. Different Scottish songs kept going round in her head, to try and find one mentioning the Isle of Skye. Eventually she had to be conventional and look at a map. They both agreed that this had been an ideal way to get to know each other, and a very exciting part of their relationship. The postman played an important role in their early romance. To see the familiar handwriting and wonder what's inside (maybe another photo as well as a letter), and then to read the writer's thoughts, ponder on them, think of a reply, and then be able to put it somewhere safe and private and read it again and again, was a great pleasure. Letters can tell so much about a person. Even the handwriting is very revealing.

I commented that Mary was living an extraordinary lifestyle, and asked Fraser how he reacted. He said he thought it was interesting, and Mary commented that her extrovert and unusual way of life had put other men off, so it was a good sign that Fraser wanted to carry on.

After three months of writing they eventually got round to phoning. Fraser's mother told him there was a call and he was very surprised to find it was Mary calling completely out of the blue. They found it delightful to talk to each other after all the letters and eagerly awaited each other's phone calls. Mary recalls perching on the kitchen table in her pokey London flat to talk, "You know, I can picture it now. I would sit on the kitchen table in the flat, my feet dangling off, and talk for ages. And all I could think of was the life Fraser had and where he was phoning from, and the dogs barking and the cows, and longing for it. Really I'd started to push my own life away, the London life, and knew instinctively that I wanted this type of life and down that phone line there came a glimmer of it, and it was joyful, and we did make each other laugh. His calls just lit up my life."

Fraser even considered getting a phone in his bedroom (an unprecedented thought as he was quite shy on the phone) since farmers generally go to bed early, and he didn't want to wake his parents. "What struck me most," he said, "Was her incredible sense of humour and her caring attitude. I thought, well, you can get a long way in life with somebody with a sense of humour. However bad things are, if you can have a laugh about it, it makes all the difference and I thought, well there's certainly a possibility here."

But then, as they realised that although this was great, both of them were completely flummoxed by the practical problems of how to have a relationship over such a distance. It was fine writing and it was lovely phoning but how do you get to know somebody physically. Would they find each other attractive? And this began to worry away, certainly at Mary, wondering how to take it to the next level.

Mary told me, "We were really worried about the next step which was having a meeting, and we had to think what would happen if we didn't click. I thought we would, knowing how well we were getting on but, I mean, he might think I was really ugly - and vice versa. The physical chemistry is so important - we have to accept that we are animals."
They found it very difficult to make the first move towards a meeting, both because of the physical distance, and because of a fear of disappointment. Both admitted that they were terrified of seeing each other for the first time. But they eventually decided that they would have a weekend together in Glasgow, which is roughly halfway time-wise between London and the Isle of Skye.

They had by now swapped photographs of each other. Fraser had bravely sent one of himself in swimming trunks and one with his new tractor, while Mary had opted for one taken several years ago in flared trousers, updated by a more rustic and appropriate shot of herself with a sheep. So, with the letters and phone calls and photos, they did have some idea of what to expect, but their hopes and fears were running high that Saturday morning when the London train pulled into Glasgow station.

Mary told me she was very nervous, but she had the actor's ability to conceal her nerves and appear outwardly confident, while inwardly she was terrified. "I wanted to look my most attractive but in control. I wore a smart suit - trousers and a bright green blazer - I guess what I would have worn to meet an important client in London. I wanted to impress him. I had heels on - not very high."

Fraser said he had never been so scared in his life. He was standing at the end of the platform and lots of people had gone past but it had got to the stage where there was only one door swinging in the wind and he still hadn't spotted her and thought she hadn't come.

Mary explained - "Well, what had happened is that I'd got off the train and I saw this chap who looked very like the photograph - you can't always tell from a photograph - and I did my usual trick. If I'm not sure it's somebody, as I come level with them I say their name. So as I came level, I said 'Fraser?' and there was no response at all. I didn't realize Mr Nervous had gone completely deaf! There was no response so I thought crickey it's not him, how embarrassing is that? I was so nervous. I walked past him and put my suitcase down and just stood there looking at his back. And I saw these rather hunky broad shoulders gradually start to fall and get lower, because he thought I wasn't on the train. He turned round very forlornly to sort of slope off, and I just looked at him and said, 'I think you're waiting for me.' And that was it."

Fraser's first response to Mary was to feel daunted by her clothes which they both described as 'London.' He had his smart leather jacket on and was feeling very well dressed by Skye standards. Later he admitted he had found her manner rather 'cold' and she had said that this was how she sometimes came across when she was trying to cover her nervousness with super-confidence

Anyway, they somehow managed to get themselves off the station and into Fraser's car. He had carefully planned the weekend with some sightseeing and hotels booked for the two nights, one in Glasgow and one in Fort William.

Mary had complicated matters by trying to do business while she was in Glasgow. She had made arrangements to meet a new client, an up and coming comedian who lived there. Unfortunately, he was good looking and charming, and Fraser's jealousy was immediately aroused. In a way, with hindsight, this was probably not a bad thing. There's nothing like a bit of competition to spur a man into action!

They had a disastrous meal at an awful Chinese restaurant. Neither could eat anything and Fraser's hands were literally shaking. They then went to the cinema to see, most appropriately, 'Mrs Brown' - the film about Queen Victoria and her Scottish manservant. They dropped the popcorn all over the floor. It had not been a very good start. Both said that, during those first few hours, they had kept looking at the other thinking, 'Is this the person I'm going to marry?'

Mary told me, "This was so different from a usual first date. There was so much subtext. But, because of the way we were introduced via your agency, we knew we were telling the truth, and that we both wanted to get married and have children. We knew that about each other before we met and we'd had six months of preparation. This was very important and we both wanted it to be right, and it was very strange - just like one of those arranged marriages. This is what is so refreshing about your agency. You know where somebody is coming from. There are no games, no messing about and nobody's lying."

By the end of that first day together they still hadn't touched and went to their separate beds, exhausted and still wondering what would happen.

The next day they drove to Fort William. Mary described her feelings. "We had to get to know each other and it was too important to mess it up. The Scottish air hit me and I kept falling asleep in the car. I kept looking at Fraser in the driver's seat and wondering, "Can I spend my life with this man?" There were tiny little white blobs on his ears (I can't even see them now), and I thought, there's no way I can spend the rest of my life with him. I thought his face was too small. Of course it isn't but I got fixated with this. I kept wondering what he thought of me."

But they had a good time wandering around the hills and lochs of Glencoe, gently flirting and getting to know one another.

They spent that night in an awful hotel. Fraser had booked a double room. Mary described how, before their meal, they were getting ready together in the same room. Fraser was polishing his shoes, and Mary was sitting at the dressing table putting her earrings on, and she remembered quite clearly thinking, "We're going to be doing this for the rest of our lives!" It was a flash of certainty. It felt completely comfortable and right. Here was a man I'd met twenty four hours ago, and we were about to go to supper. We had not touched really and yet this felt so comfortable."

The meal was a disaster, but afterwards they went up to their room and consumed a good deal of malt whisky (described by Mary as the shy person's friend) and gradually they came to share their first kiss, and their first night together as lovers.

Well, Jane Austen would have finished her story a bit after the first kiss I suppose, but for Fraser and Mary there were many more tests.

Having discovered that they were probably falling in love, they now had to go back to their real lives, five hundred miles apart. Fraser said how incredibly painful it was saying goodbye, and they had to do this many times before they finally lived together. He said that the person doing the travelling has an easier time than the person left behind, because the traveller has to concentrate on the journey whereas the one left behind can only mooch around and think of the loss and the loved one getting further and further away.

After their first meeting, Mary finalised her plans to move back to the family farm in Snowdonia. Her mother was ill and not going to recover. Fraser made the journey to Wales and was initiated into the family by being asked to cut the pigs' trotters! It was pouring with rain, Fraser recalled; not unusual of course in Wales, and something he would eventually have to get used to.

Mary also made the journey to the Isle of Skye, and loved the place. She commented on the number of very attractive men there and lamented the fact that many might face the same problems that Fraser had in finding a partner.

After a year or so of going back and forth they were both feeling frustrated by being so far apart, but while Fraser was ready to make a move, Mary was having doubts. Fraser went to Wales, wanting to propose, but when Mary met him off the train, he said he could sense her apathy. He said it was sort of, 'Oh you're here then,' not joyful at all.

Mary recalled some of the details. "Fraser wanted to get me out of the house, somewhere romantic. He wanted to go for a walk. And I was worried about what he wanted to do. I didn't know if he was going to propose and I wanted to put it off. I was rejecting the relationship a bit at that time because I was scared it was getting too serious. I was in a very strange mood, probably hormonal. Getting me out of the house was like getting a limpet off a rock. Eventually he got me out and we went to feed the sheep. We'd gone through the gate, in our mud soaked waterproofs. I stood there dripping and he got down on one knee and proposed. It was lovely up on the mountainside and I did say yes, although I was confused."

She asked Fraser not to tell anybody. To explain this unusual request she said "I had this conflict, common to my generation of women, about commitment and career, wondering if this is the right person and being scared. I said yes, but my mind was whirling. The trouble is, we're all fed a diet of knights in shining armour, whereas, here is this probably decent, good looking, nice man who I'm terribly comfortable with, but it's not fireworks and parties every night and travelling round the world. Maybe my knight in shining armour is round the next corner. But the guy who produces the fireworks is not the guy you want to spend your life with. The comfortable alternative has sometimes put people off because we sort of want to live on the edge. What I've learnt now is that companionship, trust and laughter are so important and it seems 'fuddy duddy,' but it's not, it's real. And we do have our firework moments."

I do get a lot of this sort of attitude from women (and men) in their thirties and forties. They find it almost impossible to make a commitment in case something better turns up along the line. I don't really know what the answer is here, but in my experience, for marriage or a long term relationship to work, in almost every case there has to be give and take, compromise and a willingness to take the long view.

But at this point Fate put on her gumboots and waded right in. Exuberant celebrations (Dutch courage maybe?) led to Mary becoming pregnant. But, far from this being a disaster for her, it put everything in perspective, and she was absolutely certain that marriage was right. This, for her, was a message, saying this is Mr Right. Without that, she admitted that she would probably still be trying to make up her mind.

Mary didn't want to tell Fraser over the phone, and she didn't want to tell her parents before Fraser, so she had a terrible time. They were going through lambing which is very dangerous for pregnant women as they can pick up a virus from contact with the lamb foetus. If it gets into the woman's bloodstream it can have adverse consequences for the unborn child. She was putting on gloves to deliver lambs and her parents thought this was a bit strange.

They met up again in Glasgow and went to the same awful Chinese restaurant where again they couldn't eat a thing, and Mary broke the news. Fraser was very surprised. Amazingly it was something he hadn't considered. But of course, like Mary, he felt it made the decision to marry so much easier.

I was amused at the statement 'Something he hadn't considered' and smiled at the power of human nature. Here were two intelligent human beings who had travelled well and been successful in their lives, who certainly witnessed the facts of life everyday and had possibly made mature decisions on how to conduct their love life. But against all that, old human nature comes along and does what she has been doing for centuries; informs us that we are not going to get the better of her and she will show us who is boss.

Mary described the next few months as 'Staggering through fog.' She said "We kept seeing problems that seemed insurmountable, and then, when it was right, the fog cleared and we could see how to take the next step. We had two farms, both of which would be nice to farm. Fraser's parents wanted us to farm there, and my parents wanted us to farm here. But my mother was dying, and we were all too aware of the trauma we faced. So we had all these problems; my mum's illness, having the baby and constantly worrying about how we would actually settle down and have a life together. We knew we would be upsetting one party or another wherever we decided to farm."

All their wedding preparations were made long distance. They had to meet up to choose a wedding ring. Mary's mother did a lot of the organizing. Mary said, "I found that I was able to relax and not think it was anything to do with me, and I think it's a good bit of advice for brides with mothers like mine. Fraser and I quite fancied a nice quiet Quaker wedding because it's my faith, and Fraser's quite shy. It would have suited us, but Mum wouldn't have that. Then it dawned on us that what she was planning was her own farewell party. As it turned out it was the right thing and the best party ever. It was a brilliant day. Her present to us was the fireworks at the end of the wedding. And the whole mountainside was lit up. It was a spectacular, glorious send-off; a celebration of her life and our marriage. Fraser's father very kindly paid for our honeymoon as a wedding present. I remember watching the sunset on the rocks in Ibiza. We knew we had a very bumpy time ahead of us, with my mum's health, the dilemma of where we were going to farm, a child on the way - only three months left of just the two of us. So we were in the extraordinary circumstances of having spent so little time together as a couple without children. But we knew we could share it together. The vicar at the wedding asked everybody to rally round us because of the rough ride ahead. And people have. They have been fantastic. Everybody loves the story of how we got together and it inspires people."

Instead of Fraser and Mary returning to the Isle of Skye after their honeymoon, they decided to go to live in Wales. It was quite difficult for his mother because he had said that they would go back to Skye once things were resolved in Wales, but they did not know how long that would be. So decisions had to be made about getting a permanent farm worker to replace Fraser or to get somebody who'd help part time. What actually happened was that the person in the farm bungalow said he would do the feeding and so they left it at that.

They rented a small house close to the farm in Snowdonia and they very much enjoyed being alone together for the first time. Three months later, a daughter was born - very quickly, on the living room floor. They did not come close to putting all their detailed plans for a water birth at the local hospital into effect. As it turned out, the postman alerted everyone and within half an hour their first born came into the world with Mary lying on newspapers which had quickly been spread all over the floor and with half the village in attendance!

The baby was a joy to them all, especially Mary's mother, who by then was spending most of her days in bed, through her illness. She was able to nurse the baby for many hours and developed a lovely and very special rapport with her new little granddaughter knowing full well that she would not live to see her grow up.

As the months went by it became more and more urgent to make some serious decisions, primarily about where they would live. "We both saw the problems," Mary told me, "But Fraser had faith that they would be resolved. There's an expression which goes,'What's for you won't go by you' and he kept quoting that to me."

Fraser's very wise comment was 'It's hard to take too many bridges at once. You can't do it. You're looking at a great stack of bridges, and you think I can't do it. But if you take them one at a time you can.'
"He was right," Mary acknowledged. "We could do it but if we took it step by step and what's so nice," added Mary, "Is that we're crossing those bridges together now and of course all sorts of other problems come up in our lives, but it's so nice to have a partner to walk side by side with across that bridge. It makes it a lot easier."

Mary's mother died a few months after the arrival of their new daughter. She had been a woman of great energy, strength and wisdom and the local farming community had held her in high regard. For Mary and Fraser, who had grown to love her dearly, it was hard to let her go but they learnt to do this with time.

As the months went by they felt that in order to make a decision as to where to farm they would need to spend time in both places. But then Mary fell pregnant again and they decided to stay in Wales for the birth because if they had been on Skye, she would have had to go to the mainland, and in an emergency the journey would have to be done in the lifeboat. After the birth of their little son, they courageously set out for a year in Scotland.

Fraser went up with a van with all their belongings. It's about a 10 hour drive without a stop, then onto a ferry for another hour. You can't just drive and get on the ferry as you have to wait. So it's about a full day, door to door. On the way back the van broke down at 3 o'clock in the morning.

They had a bungalow on the farm in Skye and joined in the local life. Then, in spite of being on the pill, Mary was pregnant again. The local doctor, hearing her history, commented in good dry Scottish fashion, "My, we are fertile, aren't we?"

They faced a dilemma, but they also felt they were very lucky, as they had to decide between two beautiful farms. In the end they chose to live in Snowdonia for practical reasons. Fraser said, "Probably the deciding factor was the long term financial prognosis. Farming is going through such bad times and to farm on an island is doubly hard because everything you bring in you pay for - probably about three hundred pounds to bring a lorry load of hay over on the ferry. You have to take your stock off to market. The buyers know you're from an island and you won't want to be taking them back, so you get rock bottom prices." Mary added, "And because this is Snowdon, it is attracting environmental schemes. There's more potential here. We really had to make the decision on those grounds. And for children, the opportunities on the island were less. People do survive there very well, but we had a choice."

So the lonely farmer from a remote Scottish island and the actress from London had a happy ending (although nothing ever really ends). While I was interviewing them the children wanted attention, there was farm work waiting, dinner to get ready, and a hundred other things to do. But, for one moment, I saw Mary standing by the Aga with her baby in her arms and the other two at her feet and I knew it was the image of contentment she had always wanted.

Fraser and Mary were determined to be part of this book, and to share their story to encourage others in their search for a partner.

7
The North Wind Doth Blow.....

I don't want pig farmers to feel I put them all in the same category as the pig farmer I had to chastise for smelling absolutely awful early on in this book. Far from it. I think that the great majority of farmers, and particularly pig farmers, turn out to be exceedingly presentable, virtually smelling of roses when they go out.

I certainly remember one pig farmer, Jeremy, as being one of the sweetest smelling, nicest people I have ever met. He was absolutely sincere with no false pretensions. He had a few flaws but don't we all. His were not great and he was quite honest about them.

He came to the Bureau for an interview one day in late September. His marriage had ended after about twenty years, mostly, I think, due to his lifestyle. Through being by himself for a number of years he had got into a muddle with the farm paperwork and the house.

He was an intelligent, cultured man, and, as well as being a farmer he was a Boy Scout leader, a role which he enjoyed very much. No matter what the work load was on the farm or how difficult the rest of his life became he was determined to carry this on as it was his one outlet from the day to day grind of farm work.

He sat down in one of my big comfortable chairs and said, "I'm going to ask you to do the impossible."

"Go ahead," I said," I love a challenge."

"Well, I'd like you to find my dream woman. I'd like her to be around my age, petite in build and to be able to help me with my paperwork. It would be so good if she knew about pig farming and could help out with that as well and get my house tidy and presentable again. Oh, and not live too far away. I just haven't got the time to travel a great distance. I would love to meet someone who would also understand about my enjoyment of the Scouts."

"Yes, that is all quite challenging," I said and took a deep breath, following with "Very challenging, in fact." We went on talking and then I started looking through my register. I was by myself in the admin room of the office and I had left Jeremy in the interview room drinking coffee.

There and then, looking through my register, I found Ellie and wondered if she could be the woman for him. Of course you can't tell immediately, for you can get all the factual things right but in the end the physical chemistry has to be there as well.

She lived about eight miles from him and as I kept reading things got better. She was a farm secretary, a farmer's daughter and she had described how her father mostly kept pigs, and last but by no means least she was a Girl Guide leader! I just about fell off the office chair - they're not very stable at the best of times are they? I actually could not believe it. This last attribute actually stopped me in my tracks. I thought he must know her, being so close and connected with the guides.

When I started to tell Jeremy about Ellie, his eyes lit up and he exclaimed, over and over again, "No I don't know her, I don't, really, I don't."

That afternoon a very satisfied Jeremy left my office. As he left, he had to walk round a huge heap of straw that had been delivered in the previous hour or two. Several trailer loads had been deposited, but as it was after milking and the men had gone home John had the whole lot to stack by himself. Jeremy started talking to John and without any hesitation said he was going to stop and help stack it all away. It was an incredibly kind gesture and they both worked well into the evening.

The most marked thing about autumn with us is that we have loads and loads of straw delivered, usually at the most inconvenient moments, but it all has to be stacked away for bedding through the winter.

I don't think any livestock farmer enjoys autumn for they are continually thinking that winter is just around the corner with all the work that it brings. However no one can deny the splendour of this season, especially when the low sun twinkles through the trees that surround our farm, highlighting all the tones of green, rust and gold.

Our trees are specifically placed in a horseshoe shape around the house and buildings, obviously planted many years ago to shelter us from the north. Then radiating away across the fields, are other woods curving around in an arc that acts as a wind break. Having many acres of woodland we are able to keep ourselves going in logs throughout the winter but it takes about two to three weeks continual sawing of the fallen trees to stack enough wood to see us through.

I'm sure there are some of you who may visualise me at this time of year as a typical farmer's wife, continually picking and freezing and jamming soft fruit. Well, I used to, but I was never so pleased as when one year some adolescent young stock blustered their way into the orchard and trampled down those damned blackcurrant bushes which, I'm delighted to say, have never recovered.

In the course of time Jeremy and Ellie were introduced and it turned out that her father had just retired from pig farming and was at his wits end to find something to do. As time went by I was told that as Ellie's father got to know Jeremy through his daughter, he started coming around to the farm most days to give Jeremy a hand. It certainly helped Jeremy and gave Ellie's father something to do in his retirement. And of course she put his paperwork right with her farm secretarial expertise.

The next phone call I got was from Ellie herself. She told me that Jeremy's house was really not as bad as he'd made out. "In fact, once I'd cleaned up the smelly socks and dust I actually discovered it was really beautiful."

About six months afterwards Jeremy phoned me and asked if he and Ellie could call in to see me. When they turned up about a week afterwards they announced with beaming smiles and hugging each other that they had had a quiet registry office wedding and this was the third day of their honeymoon. Ellie's father had moved into the farmhouse for a week to look after the farm. They were in a dream-like state of deep happiness and possibly the most perfectly matched pig farmers in the world!

Of course it doesn't go right every time. A few weeks after this another farmer came for an interview. A vegetable merchant with a small farm - he actually brought me several sacks of potatoes and an assortment of vegetables as a gift. He explained that he was on his way to deliver a consignment of vegetables to a new customer. I presumed that was why he turned up in his large commercial van. He was a straightforward man who, after a few weeks, received his first introduction. It came as a surprise, though, when she telephoned me the day after their first date and said she didn't want to see him again. I'm always a little apprehensive when I hear these words - what awful things have happened?

"He arrived in his big vegetable van, and when I climbed inside the only place for me to sit was on a sack of potatoes where the passenger seat should have been! I was supposed to happily bounce all evening on this bag of potatoes as he drove round doing his deliveries!"

Thinking of potatoes always reminds me of bonfire night when the children were small. The men would build a mound of wood and rubbish all week and in the evening many of the children's friends and their parents came along and we all sat around the fire on straw bales watching the fireworks at the bottom of the field. I lit a smaller fire and cooked all the food. A parent brought a guitar and serenaded us as we toasted our feet and faces and then all turned round for our backs to warm as well.

Tupping time is always around bonfire night on our farm. This is when we put the male ram with the female ewes so they can go forth and multiply the following spring. One late autumn day, Richard and Charlie, our two farm workers (a classic duo of the experienced teaching the inexperienced) put the ram in with his new harem of ewes. Wow! He thought all his Christmases had come at once. There was no thought of foreplay - instant action was on the agenda and he immediately mounted one sheep after the other in the course of about ten minutes. Charlie had stopped to light his baccie and he and Richard were leaning on the gate taking in the action. Then, without any warning, the stud of the day instantly fell down dead! Charlie took in the scene and he turned slowly to Richard who was standing open-mouthed. "Now let that that be a lesson to thee lad. Pace thyself - if thou does the same thing as yon ram, thou'll end up dead as well."

As we come closer to Christmas the Bureau office gets busier. Sadly, people realise they will be alone over this holiday time and seem desperate to find a partner quickly. They remember seeing other couples having such a good time together and cannot stand the thought of being left out for yet another year. Christmas time seems to emphasise the family bliss that we are all supposed to enjoy and when you are not in that situation but want so much to be, your whole life seems completely empty. I know of one farmer who always leaves the farm for his married brother to look after, and goes away on holiday abroad at Christmas just so he does not have to face the continual sorrow of being alone.

About two weeks before Christmas I stop sending letters out and constantly telephone people instead - it concludes introductions more quickly. I would never want anyone to be waiting over the holiday time for the information needed to get in touch with a suitable partner.

The evening of the last working day before the Bureau office breaks for Christmas has always been our evening to have a good 'girlie' night out together. My secretaries and I will have a long lingering meal out and reminisce over the work we have completed that year, with the humour that all offices experience when dealing with people. Secretaries who had left a few years previously would also be invited and would ask about remembered clients. Sometimes we would invite the farm staff and the Bureau staff to join together and that would be absolutely hilarious throughout the whole evening with their jibes, taunting and jokes.

Christmas Day on the farm is really not very much different from any other weekend day. The milking and feeding still have to be done, but we always try to make sure   everything is finished as early as possible on Christmas morning. Usually all the men would have these holiday days off except Harold, and he would virtually beg to be able to come in on Christmas Day to milk. He has a large and close family living nearby but he said he could not stand sitting in the house all day having nothing to do. He is a tall thin man who never says a lot. When he does speak it is sensible and to the point but you could go for days without having a conversation with him. We have never been sure how old he is but he has worked for us for twenty two years with virtually never a day's sickness. All his sons have worked for us too, either full time or casually, over the years and we have gone through our family difficulties with him and his wife; they were always there for us when we had troubled times. You could set your watch by his work. If you saw Harold getting the cows in or completing some other task you knew exactly what time it was as he would never vary his routine for even a minute.

Charlie has worked for us full time longer than anyone. He is about 6ft 3ins with a closely cut beard and seems larger than life. He is no fool and is actually the wittiest person I know. Faced with any situation he can always come up with remarks to make you rock with laughter. Lynda, the good looking secretary I mentioned earlier, was on the end of the phone when the farm was struck by lightning. She received quite a shock and went running over to the men's room for safety and a cup of tea to steady her nerves. Charlie told us next day that he "adopted the two principles of first aid. I made her lie on the floor and loosened her clothing." "A bit of wishful thinking, if ever I heard it," Lynda said the next day.

He is the first to admit he's not an academic and from time to time reminds us all that, "Without thick buggers like me shovelling shit the world would come to a stop." Of course he's right. We can't all be university graduates and we will always need good basic practical men like our Charlie.

The best duo we ever had on the farm was when Richard was also working for us. There was an age gap of about twenty years between Richard and Charlie, Richard being the younger. They verbally bounced off each other in a fantastically funny repertoire. A few minutes into their company and you would be in fits of laughter.

Richard is a big broad lad, about six foot two inches with a round, ruddy face. He would be the first to admit that he was not a walking encyclopaedia but he had a heart of gold and you could trust him with your life.

He talked at length one morning to Charlie about a complaint he had and maybe he should go and see the doctor.

"Oh! You've got gonorrhoea, mate," Charlie said to him.

"What's that?" asked the bewildered Richard.

"It's best to go and tell Pat what's wrong. Tell her about it and she'll have a look at you and put you right."

Richard promptly came to me in the house and said he needed some advice. As he sat down at the kitchen table he announced "I've got gonorrhoea."

I immediately thought that this was a first and went into my 'nothing can surprise me mode' and after a few moments blurted out "I'm so sorry Richard. How do you know?"

"Well, it's painful" he said, "will you have a look at it?"

Well, I knew I was the elected first aider for the farm and a nurse to boot but this was a bit beyond the call of duty.

"I don't think so," I said. "Best see your doctor."

"If you say so", he said. "But I'll have to have time off work and I thought if you could have a look at it down there and see what you think."

At that moment he angled his ear up against my face. "Down there," he said. "Just look down my ear. I think I've got some wax in it."

Only then did I fully comprehend and twigged to the mischief Charlie had been up to.

"Who mentioned gonorrhoea to you Richard?" I asked.

"Charlie. He said I'd got it in my ear."

In the winter a livestock farmer is usually pleased with a mild frost to harden the earth so he can spread his muck easier, without the continual tractor work damaging his ground. Yes, farming in the stock areas is still made up of muck, slurry and smell. Many days are taken up scurrying around spreading the stuff here there and everywhere. One day Richard was doing this task with our slurry tanker. This is the vile smelling raw runny manure collected directly from the cubicle sheds where the dairy herd are housed in the winter. As with so many things that Richard touched it went all wrong and a 'blow back' occurred. He stood in the yard with every square inch of him covered from head to foot in this foul smelling excrement, dripping in large blobs over the ground. He looked just like the monster from the deep as he stood there with only his white teeth contrasting against the huge mass of brown muck.

A few years ago at the end of January there was such a bad frost that after thawing out the water pipes there was hardly any time left in the day for the routine jobs of milking, mucking out and feeding, let alone spreading muck. Once you'd done everything the pipes had frozen again, so like the Forth Bridge you were constantly going back to the beginning to start again.

You know when you are over one thousand feet up that it would be a miracle if you got through a winter without snow, and you know that the snow will possibly bring long days full of backbreaking hard work. Other people, those in the low lands and non-farmers, might look on snowfalls with glee and anticipation. The Christmas card picture fills their minds. Instead the dour consequences are all that the livestock farmer can bring to mind and these he knows all too well; extra work.

The last week of January always starts to give you a glimmer of hope. The days are lengthening and sometimes the snowdrops at the end of our drive start to show and this is meant to fill you with anticipation of the spring to come. The men say 'Snowdrops are out - it'll soon be spring', but we all know that we are trying to deceive ourselves. On such a day in late January a few years ago, exclamations of 'Did you see the snowdrops?' came from all and sundry. But Mother Nature had a cunning surprise up her sleeve. By ten o'clock on that morning fluffy little snowflakes had started to drift across our view. How pretty they look, I thought, but of course would not have dared utter such sentimental rubbish to John for he would have quite forcefully told me where to stick such daftness.

By eleven'o'clock it was settling and the air was thick with the snow flakes that were now not so fluffy but downright large and thick, turning the whole skyline into a white haze. Without any warning the wind got up and when you ventured just into the farmyard little whirlwinds of blinding snow wrapped around you. As the men struggled around the corners of the buildings great sheets of windy snow would envelope them. I retreated to the house with my full buckets of coal and baskets of wood just as John appeared with the three workmen.

"We're going to get those heifers from up the fields - if we can get 'em to walk down through all this." The men came in to put on coats and gloves - you never know with the stubbornness and cussedness of animals how long they will be out.

I could not take my eyes from the windows. How quickly it seemed to be settling! I made the main decision about what had been bothering me. Yes, I would go and get the children from school because, at this rate, if I left it for another hour or two the school bus would not be able to get up to the village. I phoned the school and they seemed quite surprised. "Well, there isn't much snow here in Bakewell, Mrs Warren - just a few flakes." I explained that we are many hundreds of feet higher than them, but only with absolute insistence on my part, was I reluctantly believed and a promise was made that the children would be summoned to be waiting for me.

For anyone not too happy about driving in snow thank God for 4 X 4 vehicles. The Toyota pick-up is the best to use and I set off on the most direct route to the school. The roads were thickly covered with snow by this time so I had to be very cautious because for several days there had been severe frost and they were now extremely icy. My dread is actually driving downhill and losing control of the vehicle. I know I am a wimp on these occasions. I have to drive down a steep valley and across over the river. Yet it is so beautiful and transformed into a magical winter landscape. With a pheasant or two jumping out onto the stone bridge it could easily win any Christmas card competition.

The children were astounded at the SOS message to wait in the bus bay for their mother to pick them up. They were gleeful and delightfully happy to have such an unexpected half holiday. I drove back through the village and stopped to get some bread. Of course the children decided that emergency rations definitely included sweets.

As we drove out of the village I knew I had a long steep hill to ascend so I decided to get as much momentum as possible and drive through the village at the highest speed I dare go. About a third of the way up I came across a car that was sliding back down. I'm afraid I passed it and felt a little guilty but I knew that by sliding back down it would eventually come into the village and be fine.

At last we were home. I couldn't see the farm, however, because by now the whole landscape had become a 'whiteout' and with the wind and heaviness of falling snow you could only see a short distance in front.

We all got into the house and I of course first made the fire, mopped up the snow falling from our coats and shoes and thought of the meal I must get. Normally it would be something really gut hugging and hot in this weather but I didn't have enough time. John and the men were at the door and crowding into the utility room. "We can't get the buggers to turn down and walk into the wind heading down into the buildings. We've tried everything." And as he says this from the door I see they are like three snowmen - absolutely covered!

"We're going to take some food up to the stock after dinner and see what we can do when this wind dies down. We've got to start thinking about the milk tanker too. If it can't get to us we've got to get the emergency tanks out."

Soaking wet gloves and caps were put on and around the Rayburn to dry as quickly as possible and the melting snow dripped into puddles on the floor and onto the cat sitting by the Rayburn. Shall I reveal to you that the cat and I do not get on? We have a constant dislike of each other; she knows it and I know it, but when John sits down she immediately goes and sits on his lap and looks at me as if she is saying "I'm on his lap, you aren't. He prefers me to you."

I quickly got together soup, bread and cheese. The kids complained because they had missed some great school dinners. "I was going to have chow mein today," Ben proclaimed and Sarah protested that her favourite prawn cocktail lunch is not on the farmhouse menu. "Tough luck!" I exclaimed or words to express the fact that I don't feel much sympathy for their situation.

The wind continued to howl and the snow was falling even faster, so we decided to telephone around to see where the milk tanker had got to. It was located between us and Ashbourne where it had become bogged down on a farm drive and couldn't move. Colin, who was the milk tanker driver and had collected our milk for seventeen years, was the most dedicated of men. He would move heaven and earth to get through to a farm, whatever the weather. But obviously, even these conditions had got the better of him.

This is the most worrying thing about dairy farming. If you can't get your milk away you don't get paid for it and all your work literally goes 'down the drain.' John, the men and I talked about what was to be done.

"We'll have to get the emergency tankers out. We can pump the milk out of the normal tank into the emergency tank so there is enough space for the milking this afternoon," said John as he also directed one man to go and take fodder to the heifers up in the fields, one man to bring the emergency tank to the dairy door and he himself went to find and sort out the required pump. Ben volunteered to go up the fields with Charlie. Sarah wanted to build a snowman and I was told I'd be needed outside soon.

I made up the fire again, went and fetched more coal and wood and considered what to get them for the next meal. Also on my mind was the possibility that the men might not be going home that night. Then John put his head round the door with a great blast of cold air and said I'd got to go and stand outside and hold the pump by the emergency tank to make sure the milk was transferred without too much spillage. Harold and Richard were sent to start the routine jobs that were usually finished about midday.

The wind got even worse as I stood by the tank. I couldn't believe how bad it was and yet I was sheltered. Whatever was it like on the exposed hillside? My fingers were numb, my eyes stinging from the constant battering of snow flakes. I dreamt as I stood there that my toes were in front of my lovely roaring fire and I was getting hotter and hotter. Of course the reality was the absolute opposite. At last, after standing and holding the pump about a foot in the air for an hour the transfer was over and we had an empty milk tank. The milking started a little later than usual, but how lucky that this had gone so well. John said he hoped the men had done the essentials and then they would start milking. Harold would get the cows out of the cubicle shed. They had to come into the collecting yard adjacent to the shed and then walk into the milking parlour. Only a few yards but with the biting wind heading straight at them they would not be keen to even come out of their housing.

Back in the house I thought of the hot meal for later. I was sure there would be three extra men - seven of us in total. A stew, I thought but then there was not enough time to tenderise stewing steak or shin of beef. It would have to be a casserole using some better beef. Quickly I got the ingredients together and I decided to do an enormous rice pudding. I put all this in the oven and after about half an hour the next surprise occurred.

The electricity went off. Was it me? No I hadn't done anything. By that time it was dark so I floundered for matches and candles. Noises came from the back door.

"Telephone to see if it's the mains or us." On outlying farms it's quite a common thing for the electricity to go and I know the telephone number by heart. "Yes, quite a lot of your area is without electricity," was the reply.

John's decision was that it would be best to put on our own generator and get the cows milked. When the generator is being used for milking we can't use it for anything in the house but for one or two lights. At least the meal will still cook with the retained heat of the Rayburn, I thought.

There was a knock at the door and I stood in shock as I knew no ordinary vehicle could get up our drive and contemplated for a few seconds who on earth it could be. On opening the back door a figure like the abominable snowman stood, breathless and trembling, covered from head to foot in snow and obviously freezing to death. It was Colin, our milk tanker driver. He walked in and started to tell me that he had managed to get from his Ashbourne collections to our area but had not been able to get his vehicle up the hill, to us. So he had decided to walk from the bottom of the hill to our farm to ask John to take the tractor down to his milk tanker and pull him up.

"Never mind that," I said, "Have you had anything to eat all day?" He admitted that he had not and that he was starving. "Well you are not doing anything until I've cooked you something," I announced. Knowing that the Rayburn would still have some heat I set to and I quickly cooked bacon, sausage, eggs and fried bread washed down by tea.

With his clothes warmed and food and drink inside him he seemed a different man. Colin had been collecting our milk for many years. He always had a friendly word with you most mornings when he came onto the farm, never chatting too long or gossiping about others. He had such dedication to his dairy farmers and kept trying, no matter what the weather, to get to them and take their milk to ensure that their hard working efforts in milk production would be paid for.

With a determined spirit Colin went outside to arrange with John for the help he needed. I heard a tractor set off and after a while the tanker trundled into the yard. Once again in the midst of whirling snowflakes the milk was transferred from the milk tanks. Our tractor pulled it down the drive and continued escorting it for a few miles until it got on to the main road and was able to slowly but eventually get the milk back to the depot. Thank God for men like Colin, salt of the earth with a highly committed and dependable spirit.

After what seemed an interminable amount of time all the men once again came like snowmen into the house and peeled off their outer layers of clothing.

"Well I can't see any of you going home tonight," said John. "The thing is if you went home there is the real chance if it continues to snow like this you will not be able to get here tomorrow when I shall need you more than ever."

There was a fair bit of muttering before the men agreed that John was right. The meal was eaten by the flickering light of candles and then we discussed the sleeping arrangements. Although we have a guest bedroom, with no electricity we couldn't heat it, so it was decided they would all sleep in the sitting room with a settee each and toast themselves in front of the fire.

At first light the next day it looked as if it hadn't snowed much more and the storm had blown itself out. What a relief! I started to think about my plans for the following day. I had made arrangements to visit Pauline and Jim on their farm in Lancashire, so maybe I could still go.

8.
A Nice Guy

I started out from Mere Farm to visit Pauline and Jim and the first few miles of the journey were quite difficult. There were no other vehicles on the hilltops, just oceans of snow. It actually got worse for a few miles as I negotiated the hazardous road leading past the Cat and Fiddle, the highest pub in England, but as I descended into the Cheshire plain the snow immediately disappeared. By the time I'd got into Lancashire the sun was shining and there was no evidence that back in Derbyshire we were in the depths of winter!

Pauline and Jim had a fairly large farm in the fertile lowlands of Lancashire, a short distance from the coast. I was greeted with a hug from both and exclamations of "Why have you driven all this way in the farm 4X4?" I explained about the snow and Jim said they had had some lovely sunny days and he'd been playing golf all the day before."

I thought they both looked at me as if I had dreamt up the last few days but Pauline reassured me that she knew how different it was up in my part of the world. She reminded me that she had lived 'up high' for ten years. I told them we'd had frost and snow and that the milk tanker had not been able to get through and the electricity had been cut off. Then I looked around and had to admit it seemed a world away here at Jim's arable farm.

I was taken into the long farmhouse. This had been the original farm building. Constructed in ornate brick, they had retained the centuries old features such as the large double doors for the horse wagons which were now a huge window spanning two floors.

They looked quite alike. Of course one was male, tall and masculine and one was female, short and feminine. They both had friendly, ruddy, rural faces, the same blond hair and both were slim in build and in their forties.

I asked Jim what first attracted him to Pauline and he said straight away without having to think, "Well I have really always thought that I would speak to anyone you asked me to, no matter what I thought of their profile. When I did talk to Pauline for the first time I was quite impressed at how normal she seemed."

Pauline said that when she read Jim's profile she was quite pleased that he had interests other than farming. I remembered her saying to me in her first week as a bureau member, "I've got life in me and I want to meet someone with a bit of life as well." Pauline went on to admit that she had always loved farm life but never wanted to exclude the possibility of a life outside farming.

Jim asked her to meet him and Pauline explained that her philosophy has always been that if you spend a day with someone, even if you don't get on too well, you can still have a nice day out and part as friends at the end of it. You do not have to think, 'Well this could be the one,' but take it as a day out with a friend.

On the way to Harrogate, where they had decided to meet, a most astonishing and traumatic thing happened to Jim. His ex-girlfriend sent him a message on his mobile phone at about ten am to tell him that he was now the father of a daughter born to her at six fifteen am that morning. He had been in a relationship with this woman for about six months and it had ended about eight months earlier. He'd not met her through the Farmers and Country Bureau. The big thing was that he had never had children before so goodness what a shock for him as he did not even know she was pregnant. Pauline said, "It must have been so difficult for him to continue his journey and meet me without showing his emotions."

Before Jim arrived in Harrogate he explained how he had to stop for a few minutes to contemplate the news he'd had. "My immediate thoughts were how do I know this child is mine?" My head was really full of it, swirling around. Then I thought about Pauline and knew she would be waiting, so I drove on."

Jim kissed her on the cheek and immediately gave her a hug when they met up. She thought that was a lovely warm gesture and liked it. They decided to go and have a meal and Pauline left her car while they drove to the restaurant. When she got in his vehicle the first thing she noticed was how they had so much in common with their CD collections. Pauline sat in his car and said, "Oh I've got that, and I've got that too." This similarity continued with their talk over the lunch table. They liked eating the same things - ice cream, cream cakes - all the things you should not eat. Jim added, "I was determined not to meet someone who was paranoid about her weight and is constantly on a diet." The day ended with another kiss - a bit more lingering this time.

On the way home Pauline said to herself that this one's different. She said he felt so comfortable, a warm and affectionate person. She found this so lovely and reassuring and something that she had been missing.

They waited a fortnight before Jim visited Pauline's home. She lived in a cottage in the middle of nowhere up in the Pennines. "Back of beyond," Jim called it. "A lovely spot but so exposed, so very, very different from where I live."

He explained how he wanted to visit her home to see how she kept her house. This was important to him. He admitted he could never be with someone who didn't like a nice clean house. "Well, we both like a nice home," Pauline added.

What struck Jim when he met her again was that she was just the same as the first time. "She hadn't changed," he said. "So often over the years, I had met women who were false to begin with and changed as time went on. Pauline seemed totally unlike this."

They admitted that upon meeting this time an even more passionate kiss was exchanged. "Very nice" Jim said on reflection. They went for a walk, hand in hand and decided the only way they would get to know each other was to keep talking and say what they thought and be truthful to each other. Jim said, "What made the day for me was that when we came back after the walk she cooked me a meal, so I thought thank goodness she likes her food and is willing to cook."

They then went to meet Pauline's sister. She said how 'nice' Jim seemed to be which he cringed at and said "I hate the word 'nice.' That word conjures up quite a boring guy." "No, no," Pauline and I protested, "It means you are generally a lovely person."

Jim continued, "But doesn't that mean you're boring? You see I feel that women never usually go for the ordinary, steadfast, down to earth men, they usually go for someone who stands out from the crowd, not the nice guy."

"Well look what they are missing, "cried Pauline "I know what I prefer!"

I asked Jim about when he first contacted me and he said he first got in touch with me in 1983. He was introduced to several women and went out with one for several months but then he met a local lady who he eventually married. That marriage, he realises, was never right because he felt he was a bit on the rebound. They were actually married for twelve years but had no children. This was followed by a short relationship with the woman who had just had his child. He then decided to come back to the Bureau. "I couldn't believe you remembered me from fifteen years ago but you did."

Pauline said, "I was fed up with meeting the wrong kind of men. I always read Farmers Weekly and saw your advert week after week. I knew it was the agency that I wanted to join but I thought it was a lot of money. Then of course I thought, well, if she changes my way of life that's not expensive." She went on to describe how she had always wanted an outdoor life and for ten years she worked at a garden centre. When she was about twenty four she got married but it was a disaster because he was such a womaniser. By the time she was twenty nine he had brought the marriage to an end through his constant affairs. In her earlier years with him they tried to have a baby but nothing happened. Eventually they got around to trying IVF but those treatments did not work either.

A year or two went by after her separation and she felt so lonely. She'd meet other men and thought that maybe this is the one, only to be really disappointed when she got to know them better. Sometimes she'd think it was not worth meeting men because the constant disappointment made her feel even worse. She told me that when she got in touch with me she was very despondent. But then she added, "You've got to keep going and trying. You've got to be optimistic. There must be someone out there for you."

Jim said, "Now in my mature years I've realised that I wanted to meet a woman who had done something with her life. Pauline certainly can live independently from me. She does not want me for what she can get out of me. Sometimes I thought other women were like that."

The next time Jim went to Pauline's house he purposely sat in a single chair to begin with. He didn't want her to think he was too forward. Pauline said, "I thought he seemed a bit frosty and I thought to myself, 'Well he's got to shape himself up a bit because I can't be coping with a man who is not affectionate.' I'd had that for years previously."

I've found this quite often. Men purposely hold back in the amorous arena while the women say quietly to themselves, 'For God's sake come and get me.' Jim laughed and said how in his youth he went out with a girl for over a month before he even kissed her.

"I'd have ditched you," said Pauline.

We all laughed at this and said how much that shows that it always has to be the right person at the right time in anyone's life. Perhaps Pauline wouldn't have been right for Jim if he had met her twenty years earlier.

The third time Jim came over to her house and it got late Pauline asked if he wanted to stay over. His reply was a nervous "No." Later Jim asked if the offer was still there, and Pauline said that he could have her bed and she would have the settee. Jim replied that he only really wanted her bed if she was in it too. With a twinkle and giggle from both the atmosphere was relieved by Pauline saying OK it was a deal. Pauline continued, "I've always felt that if your sex life is good together then so many things that could be difficult will be overcome much more easily. We found it so wonderful. For the first time we both experienced the warmth and affection that we had both gone so long without. That night something far more precious than sex developed between us. We discovered a mutual bond and great tenderness."

I asked Jim about his farm and he told me he was born and brought up in the old farmhouse. His father was a farmer, and they were dairy farming until Jim damaged a cartilage in his knee and his doctor advised him to give it up. So they went arable with just over two hundred acres, tiny really by today's standards. After his dad died in 1987 Jim decided to expand and he now has three hundred and twenty acres. He had to pay two hundred thousand a short while ago for his divorce settlement and commented, "I'm sure this affects a lot of farmers today. They are very wary of getting into a committed relationship knowing that if they have to go through a divorce a lot of money has to be found, with the large assets that owning land brings."

He went on to say that when his mum is no longer there (she lives in a house close by) he feels radical changes will happen. He used to live to farm - but does not do that anymore. "I'll retire and enjoy far more golfing afternoons living off my interest. I doubt I will be farming after I'm fifty five."

In November, they started making plans for her to come over to Jim's farm for Christmas. Then, out of the blue, he said, "I could definitely live with you, you know, what about living together?"

There was a general silence from them both after telling me all this. They then went on to say that on the phone that week it was mutually agreed that Pauline would give up her job to come over permanently to live with Jim.

On reflection they realised they had only actually met seven times before they decided upon this. The day after Pauline had given up her job Jim came with a van to take Pauline and all her stuff over to the farm. By the end of that day all was packed up in Pauline's home and she had gone. "If you don't do something you never get anywhere. I thought, 'What have I got to lose?' A dear friend of mine had just died. I was devastated and thought 'Life does not go on forever. Go for it.'

I then asked them to tell me about their life together now.

"Well, Jim can be old fashioned and a bit fussy but I just let him get on with it. Sometimes I will admit that I miss my home that I spent such a lot of money on, then when Jim comes back into the house I realise with a jolt how wonderful it is to have his love and companionship and what is the point of a superbly designed home if you have no one to share it with."

Pauline gets on very well with Jim's mother. She does not approve of them living together but has come to accept it. They visit her every day and most days she cooks a meal for them. "It keeps her occupied and gives her something to look forward to," says Jim. "Oh she's lovely," says Pauline.

The one painful and sad aspect of their life is that just at the time when they are experiencing so much joy together Jim has had to face the fact that he has recently become a father to a child. By all accounts it seems that the mother used him to get pregnant then promptly left him. She has now dropped the bombshell that he has a baby daughter to support. Pauline wants to understand what Jim is going through with this and supports whatever he decides to do. Jim has never had children and Pauline realizes that if she can never give him children this will be his only chance.

"It is so unfair," says Pauline. "I would love this baby to be ours, or even be a little part of our lives in the future." But it seems this won't happen as the mother is demanding that Jim supports his daughter but is not prepared to let him see her or have her in his life.

Pauline said, "I would love to look after the baby some days but I know that will never happen." She and Jim have to balance out their lives in this respect with the reality of what will be. It does not look as if they will have children together and they have to come to terms with this sad fact.

But they are very positive about their life together. "We've found it so wonderful. For the first time in our lives we're experiencing warmth and affection, something which we've both never really known. For years we had a yearning for true love. We know now that we've found it."

Then she added, "I joke sometimes and remind him most days what good value for money he was!"

9.
Quaint Old English Customs

Most of the winter months in farming are dull, dismal and cold, especially on our upland livestock farm where the winter does not change into spring until quite late. Work appears endless as most of the livestock are inside and the time between Christmas and Easter feels like a continual grind of milking, cleaning out and feeding. These routine jobs have to be done both early in the morning and in the late afternoon, all in the unrelenting dark and very often in low cloud or fog.

The occasional crisp and sunny winter day can be quite beautiful but you are constantly looking forward to seeing those first few signs of spring. Be it buds on the trees, early daffodils, anything really which heralds that spring will be just around the corner and that the dark days will be a thing of the past. Then the fog will relent and the sun will feel wonderfully warm as you go about your business.

On these dreary, hard days, I always think my main job is to keep everywhere warm, with abundant clean and dry clothing and lots of hot food available. Yes, it is a bit of an old fashioned attitude, you are possibly saying to yourself, but for a farm and a farmer to work well and as profitably as possible you have to have these very basic essentials in place.

On the other side of the farmyard, in the Bureau office, I leave all this domesticity behind and run what I hope has always been an efficient, competent little business.

You would think that no one's thoughts would turn to love and romance in these cold months, but the atmosphere in the office in February is one of enthusiasm and usually great hope. Amazingly, it always seems one of the busiest times of the year. I have put it down to a reaction from Christmas. Many people are alone and do not want to be, so they decide to make an earnest effort in the weeks ahead. Or perhaps over Christmas an established relationship did not live up to their expectations and has now been brought to a close, with the hope that they will find a new love in the New Year.

I also find that I have always got quite a lot of publicity from newspapers, TV and radio, in that dull period just after the New Year and before the heady days of spring appear. Maybe it's because the media seem to be trying to push the romance and love angle to their readers, listeners and viewers to alleviate the depression of those dark winter days.

The article titled "Cut Price Brides" published by the Daily Express in 1986 was perhaps the most sensational in its opening lines. It emphasised to lonely Falkland Islanders that I was charging a very low price and therefore a good bargain was to be had by joining the Bureau and getting a "cut price bride."

"Introducing the Introducer" was the title of an article published by The British Farmer magazine. Looking at the photo of me that appeared in the article in 1983 I seemed to look like a virtual teenager. In fact I do recall giving them a younger photo of me - which I suppose was quite naughty.

The Yorkshire Post completed two long articles quite close together. "A Farmers' Wife With a Unique Occupation" was printed in 1986. They quoted here that I was 'only accessible by a rough track through windswept fields.' They did a follow up in 1989 which said that 'wedding invitations flutter in like confetti' and 'kittens frisk beneath the table closely followed by sheepdog Bess.' Did we have a sheepdog called Bess? We certainly didn't have kittens under the kitchen table as I can't abide cats and have always put any kittens in the engine shed where it is warm.

Going into the 1990s for their Valentine's Day issue the Mail on Sunday did a four page article titled "The Farmer Wants a Wife." Here they called me a 'jolly, roly-poly woman,' but made up for this by doing some really good in-depth interviews with two bureau members from the south and two from the north.

By 1992 the magazine Country Living did two full pages of interviews they had done with Bureau members, also calling the article, "The Farmer Wants a Wife." They described in depth the story of my client Andrew from Somerset, who was desperately lonely. Working very long hours and despairing that he may never find anyone, he poured his heart out to the journalist. But, it was frustrating to me and possibly all of those people who read his story that it was never followed up. Just one week later, Andrew met a lady who he called his 'soul mate' through the Bureau and has been really happy ever since.

The 'Farmer Wants a Wife' theme was taken up later by Country Living magazine for a television programme. I have to emphasise that I made no contribution to this at all.

Of all the newspapers The Telegraph seem to have done the most thorough articles on the Bureau. First in 1989 with "Rural Course of True Love Given a Helping Hand" then, using the title again, "The Farmer Wants a Wife" in 2002. I remember with the first article they sent a photographer to take the necessary picture. He was most insistent that I sat on a stone wall with a virtual force ten gale coming at me. I was appalled that the whole nation would see me in this dreadful state, hair even more untidy than it normally is. The second article was very well researched with thorough interviews with me and clients. This was my favourite. It was illustrated by a fabulous cartoon by 'Joe.' He had drawn the stereotype country bloke with mucky wellies, a flat cap and by his side a buxom busty wench with an apron around her ample middle. Lamb under one arm, pig under another, chickens flying in all directions, these two were striding across the farmyard blowing kisses to each other. You couldn't help but laugh your socks off at the impression it gave.

Some of the other best articles have been with regional papers. I've had good coverage in the Western Mail with "Cupid's Bow Aims at Farm Lonely Hearts," and "Exclusive Matchmaking for Country Folk." appeared in the Scottish Farmer in 1992. They described me as 'warm and motherly as if nothing would surprise or annoy her.' So, what with the roly-poly description and suggestions of being like a placid mother hen I realise I never did get my image of a vivacious sex goddess over to my public!

One of the most enjoyable interviews I have done was for the programme Home Truths presented by John Peel. They asked if they could do a piece about the Bureau and said an interviewer would be phoning me to arrange to come to the farm.

When she telephoned she introduced herself and said "You'll probably know me better as Ruth from The Archers, the wife of David Archer, one of the main characters."

I was quite surprised about this and asked if they had arranged for her to interview me due to the farming connection. Apparently not. Doing general interviews for Home Truths was her second job.

When 'Ruth' arrived, I suppose I had not expected her to be so attractive, petite and dainty and to speak with a well spoken southern accent. She explained that the Geordie accent was just for the programme. I then dived straight in to talk about farming, expecting her to be amazingly knowledgeable about agriculture as she is in her role in The Archers.

"No, no," she said, "That's just for the radio. In fact I'd be delighted to come and watch John milk. It would be one of the few times I would be really close to cows!"

I could hardly believe it as she always comes over as the complete opposite on the radio and you are always hearing her in the milking parlour. What a fabulous actress!

For the whole day she interviewed me, spoke with John, walked around the farm and got to know the cows a bit better. She recorded the gurgling sounds of the milking machines in the parlour and the crunch of us walking over the fields and the crowing of our roaming cockerel searching his territory for another female to sexually exploit. The programme sounded brilliant when it was broadcast but, having been a devoted fan of the Archers for many decades, I still can't believe that Ruth is the same un-farmish woman who visited me that day.

I've had three interviews on Woman's Hour over twenty years and spoken on numerous local radio shows. The one radio programme I refused to go on was with Robin Day, when he used to host a one pm programme on Radio Four. I just know my place I suppose and thought I would never be able to hold my own with him.

I've had American, Canadian and Japanese television companies spend the day with me filming the Bureau at work. The American company wanted to see the lives of 'typical English farmers who are looking for love.' I could only get one male Bureau member to be interviewed by them but the producer wanted to see other Bureau clients doing their 'everyday farm work.' So, we set up Charlie and Richard as being typical English farmers seeking wives. I suppose we needed our heads examined, but when you are desperate, needs must. They filmed Charlie feeding the cows in one part of the farm then they filmed a close up of him taking out his baccie tin and doing a roll up and then leaning on a hay fork.

When it came to Richard's turn, off he went to another part of the farm to make it look as if it two different farms were being filmed. John and I watched from afar then we nearly died a thousand deaths when they asked Richard if he could show them any typical English customs and he proceeded do a rendition of a Morris Dance!

Holding stems of Ragwort in both hands instead of the white handkerchiefs, (he'd probably never owned one let alone two white handkerchiefs) he started dancing up and down, swaying and jumping as he went. Large and ample, Richard was having the time of his life and the producer just loved this quaint old English custom. The programme was broadcast 'coast to coast' and so the whole American continent must now think that all English farmers act as loony as they come and are constantly dancing about their farms with plants in both hands. Richard, I know, had visions of a wealthy American heiress being so smitten with him and his dance that she would mail order for him to fly over to her instantly.

By the time Charlie and Richard had acted their parts for a Canadian film company they seemed old hands at it. They never even considered it at all an unusual diversion from their daily mucking out when a Japanese news programme stayed on the farm and filmed them. I understand Richard's local was filled with wonderment when he walked in and casually announced, when ordering his beer, that he had been on Japanese television that day.

When these programmes wished to speak to a Bureau member, someone absolutely genuine, of course, would be invited to come to the farm to be interviewed by them.

I've been asked several times to appear on Kilroy and chat shows to discuss 'the loneliness of the countryside.' I suppose the most exciting interview was in 1990 when I was interviewed live on the Wogan show. I was approached several weeks before and all was arranged for me to travel down for the day, stay in a hotel and have a limousine take me from the hotel to the television studios.

The day before I went to London the BBC telephoned me to tell me who I would be appearing with, on the programme. They told me it would be Bob Geldoff and a pop group. They said the name of the pop group but I thought I'd never heard of them before. I walked over to the farmhouse from the office and said to John and the children, "I know who I am appearing with tomorrow. It's Bob Geldoff and a pop group, I think they are called Water, Water, Water." Ben and Sarah looked at me completely silent for a few moments and then yelled, "Mum, it's not Water, Water, Water - it's Wet, Wet, Wet! Oh, you're so daft, Mum. Fancy not knowing them. Can we come, please, please, please?"

I got ready for the Wogan show at the London hotel in which the BBC had booked me. At the hotel I must admit I did start to get very nervous whilst I was waiting. Then I remembered saying to myself that if I continued to be so nervous I would make a complete hash of it and not enjoy the interview at all. So I literally made myself calm down. The limousine arrived and I was driven to the theatre where the programme takes place to be greeted at the stage door by a crowd of autograph hunters. Of course they were desperately disappointed when it was only me who alighted from the car.

I met Wet, Wet, Wet quite intimately, as they had to let me into their dressing room for a short while for me to slightly undress so the microphone could be put under my clothes. Lovely boys, they were so easygoing and friendly.

When I came out of make-up, I have to admit I looked incredibly glamorous in comparison to my normal appearance, with a wondrous hairstyle and fabulous amounts of mascara. In the hospitality room my nerves were intact until some bright spark from the production team reminded me that there could be an audience of coming up for twenty million! Suddenly I visualised everyone I'd ever known in my life watching me, especially everybody I had ever been to school with and all my old boyfriends. You imagine all the remarks that an old boyfriend from whom you parted in acrimonious circumstances twenty years ago could make. I was convinced I would reply in absolute gibberish to Wogan's questions and thinking that I would be scrutinized by the whole population, I became frightened to death. However, when I was interviewed all went exceptionally well and I enjoyed every minute of my fifteen minutes of fame. But what seems to remain in most people's memories is the fact that I undressed in Wet, Wet, Wet's dressing room.

10.
Hearts and Flowers and Sleepless Nights

The Valentine season certainly brings romance to the forefront and by the time the first week of February is over, the media and the card industry have both reminded us that, like it or not, 'love is in the air.'

One February I had a huge and elaborate bouquet of flowers delivered to my door on Valentine's Day. With overwhelming wonder and optimism I persuaded myself that John was keeping to a New Year's resolution that he had not told me about and was turning romantic in his old age. Well, I should have known that those sort of miracles don't happen. They weren't from my husband but from a devoted suitor of a lady in Devon who I had introduced a few months before. The note said that when he came to sending his true love flowers for Valentine's Day, he thought about who had brought them together and felt that I deserved some just as much. What a lovely thought! He will obviously make a charming husband

The lovely events of February tend to be engagements and weddings on Valentine's Day. I would have thought that people would aim for the warmer months but to them getting married on this special day seems so right. Nearly every year on the fourteenth of February I have an invitation from somewhere in the country to attend a wedding. If they are far away I do not accept but within a reasonable distance I certainly do.

About two years ago the BBC asked if they could feature the Bureau. I told them I would be delighted but they would have to do the interview beforehand as I was going to a wedding on Valentine's Day and wouldn't be in the office. I could virtually hear the cogs turning around in their minds when I said this, and after a pause the director asked, "Would there be any chance of us coming along with you to this wedding so we could do it as a special feature?"

"Oh! No, no," I quickly said. "They're a very shy couple who have led such quiet lives. They'd never contemplate having their wedding televised."

Well, of course the director wouldn't take no for an answer so he asked me to put it to them and see what their reaction was.

Never in a million years would this particular couple want to have anything to do with television on such a day, I thought to myself. Reluctantly I picked up the phone and when Howard answered it I very tentatively put the idea forward. Of course he didn't know what to say. Who would? He said that he wasn't sure, it was a bit of a surprise, but if I hung on he'd ask Marie, his fiancée, who was standing right next to him. There was quite a lot of muttering in the background and I prepared myself for the polite apology. To my utter astonishment, however, when the couple had made their minds up and Howard came back on the line, he said, "We've decided we'll do it, Pat, just for you. Especially if it would help other people like us get together."

After a few weeks of making these media arrangements it came about that Central News and three of the local newspapers were to be present at the wedding set for Valentine's Day 2000. It still amazed me that this quiet and discreet couple had taken this major step and said yes to all this. 'What's the harm?' they both said, 'We are so proud to be marrying each other that we want the world to know.' They had already had a little experience of the media. About a month before they got engaged at Christmas time they had sent a letter to their local newspaper, The Sentinel, encouraging anyone who would be alone at Christmas to try to meet someone special through an Introduction Agency and the paper had printed the letter. The paper then got back in touch and said they would be pleased to feature them in the future. The couple's philosophy is if it helps or encourages other lonely quiet people to join an agency and meet someone they will support it.

It was all set up for the presenter to arrive very early at the farm on Valentine's Day to interview me. They then wanted to film me getting ready for the wedding and setting off. Somehow the local TV news programme, Central News, got wind of this as well and telephoned me to ask if they could film the proceedings of the day. I thought, "Well, in for a penny, in for a pound," and spoke to the poor, bewildered couple again.

"Oh well, why not," they said, "We've both led such quiet and sheltered lives. Let's do this with a bang!"

The news programme spoke to them direct and it was arranged that they film the bride getting ready for the wedding and accompany her to the ceremony.

I organised all that had to be done beforehand. My local hat shop, Lady Fair, in Bakewell are very good. As I purchase so many wedding hats from them, I always get a little discount and a good selection. I bought a really nice hat to go with a new outfit as I thought I'd better look a bit spruced up if we were all going to be on television. I had arranged for someone to come into the farmhouse the morning of the wedding to look after the film crew and interviewer and provide breakfast and coffee whilst I went and changed for the wedding. It was all organised to the last detail right down to an early night the day before.

As John returned from his final check around his stock he announced that things didn't look too good for a peaceful night. It seemed we might have two cows that would calve in the night. I mumbled to myself that I could not believe this. I couldn't remember when we had had two cows calving together in the night before. So I put my head on my pillow muttering that I needed a good night's sleep. Don't those cows understand? "All might go well," John continued, "But I've got to go back out in an hour."

As I was just slumbering nicely John came upstairs and announced that he had got to have my help. It was not the calving cows that were in trouble, it was one that had calved previously. She unexpectedly needed to be transferred to another shed and he could not do it alone. I got up, dressed and trundled behind John putting on my old warm coat; the same coat that had provided such a good service on so many other similar, cold, dark nights. Indeed, the very same coat I had worn when avoiding my best dressed customer ever with the pram, bag lady style. Unknown to me it had started to snow so the difference at half past midnight from my warm cosy bed to this was beyond belief.

We transferred the cow with ease considering she had to walk outside in the huge snowflakes that were now falling. However, as soon as she arrived in her new quarters she 'went down' with milk fever and very quickly deteriorated. It was time to act fast and as John was administering the medicine she lashed out and kicked me, flinging me several feet away and knocking me unconscious!

"Come on, Pat," I heard as I came round. "No time to be lying down on the job. We've got problems with those calvers now." I know I saw stars that night and they weren't only in the sky! Still, I seemed to recover and went off to look at the calving cows. Sure enough, one did need help.

I'm not a tremendous amount of help in the calving itself so I get designated to the secondary status of fetcher, carrier and, in years gone by before we had mechanical help to aid calving, the puller. That meant pulling on two ropes which had been tied around the calf's ankles as they just poked out of the mother. You pulled like hell forgetting your bad back or that you might have the flu or how your arms felt as if they would tear apart and you just kept pulling with all your might. I went and fetched the calving aid and we began the task that we had done together for many years, John and I, in the middle of the night, namely bringing life to a new little calf.

Thankfully all went well, although it seemed to be a long job and by now it was about two am.

We went to look at the second calving cow on our way back to the house and could not believe it. She was in difficulties as well. So, back I went to fetch the calving aid and start all over again. This time things proved very difficult. "It's no good. We'll have to get the vet," said John. Once again I thought, "This can't be happening. I need my sleep. I'm on telly tomorrow!" But no matter how you protest to yourself or to the Almighty, it has no effect, and so I went into the house to phone the vet. Chris came out from Youlgrave, our local village, at about 3am. I waited at the yard entrance to wave him in and direct him to the appropriate shed. I'd fetched the hot water and clean towels (yes, you really do need the proverbial hot water, when birthing difficult calves). An examination revealed that a caesarean was the only option. You then just go into your routine mode of fetching a halter for the cow and more bales of straw to create a cleaner working environment both for her and us. These also provide a clean surface for the vet on which to put his implements. In addition more hot water is required and in the days of the old vet a whisky bottle would have been requested as well!

We all know where to stand and how to assist in the sterilization of the wound area and in other parts of the surgical procedure. A good healthy live heifer calf was born that night and by the time all was cleared away it was four am.

You always feel you have to invite the vet into the house to clean himself up and once there you have to ask him if he'd like a coffee no matter how tired you are. Of course if they have worked really hard you feel duty bound to offer them something to eat as well. But for once, just once, I thought maybe we wouldn't, not that morning, because at least then I could have about an hour's sleep.

But lo and behold my dearest benevolent husband said, "Are you going to have some breakfast with us before you go Chris?" This was the one time that I crossed my fingers and hoped so hard that our dear vet would say no. Sod's law of course decreed that he said, "Eh, that'd be grand."

John smiled at me as if I'd been fortunately blessed to have been allocated this task. Of course, had we not had company, I would have delighted in telling him what a burke he was and didn't he know I needed some sleep. It was no good though. I realised that and so, with a smile on my face, I started getting a full English breakfast for the household. John always got up to start milking at 5am. When that time came they both walked out, John to milk, Chris to go home and me to ponder on the fact that the TV cameras would be descending on me at seven am and I had had no sleep at all!

I decided not to think about the fact that I hadn't slept but to look forward to the day. I knew that the kitchen could be cleared and tidied by the lady who was coming in to attend to the film crew. Maybe I could close my eyes and doze for a while in the chair. Well you know what it is like when you are too tired and you know you can only shut your eyes for a short period. Everything just keeps going over and over in your mind.

I started thinking about Howard and Marie who were to be married that day and hoped they had had their beauty sleep because this was going to be the biggest event in their lives. As I rested I recalled the details of how they had come together and their whole story came into my mind all over again.

11.
The Lonely Furrow

Nik.

When Marie joined the Bureau her photograph showed her as a petite, slim lady in her early fifties with twinkling eyes accompanying her lovely warm smile. She was short, really no more than five feet, with hair that was nicely styled but had gone prematurely grey. Her nursing career had spanned thirty years and she had been through a number of positions from being a practising midwife to a ward sister and had taken early retirement.

She lived in Nottinghamshire and although her parents were not farmers many of her family were. Most of all she loved living in the countryside, hated towns and cities and seemed to have a very adaptable nature. She was obviously a caring person, but I could not get over the fact that she had not had a boyfriend for thirty years and then she only went out with someone for a few months and this had not developed into a serious relationship. "How could anyone so lovely have slipped through the net?" I thought, and after all these years of being unattached, would she ever be able to develop a loving partnership with someone? Many people who have remained single into their forties and certainly fifties think they want that committed permanent relationship. However, when they realise that it means having someone else constantly in their life to consider and live with, then sometimes they cannot accept this. But you don't know until you try. So, of course, I set to work to do my best for Marie.

Howard joined about two months after Marie. I didn't rush to match him up instantly as I was going on holiday. On the beach one day in a relaxed moment of letting any sort of thought drift into my mind, as one does, I started to think about Howard and who I could introduce him to. It was then, whilst looking out to sea, that I thought of Marie and kept that thought firmly in my mind when I returned home to my office.

On my return to work after my short break the first introduction I considered was Marie and Howard. I had spoken at length to them both but not met either of them at that stage. I deliberated in my office with Howard's form in one hand and Marie's in the other. Marie was only two months older than Howard so the age seemed fine but he was considerably taller; about fourteen inches taller actually, which most people feel is too much of a difference. Tall men, that is men over six feet, usually prefer taller women and I like to keep men of this height for the ladies of five feet ten and over.

Howard was a well built man with glasses and a slightly receding hairline. Not too distinguished you might say. You could be right but he had a lovely, friendly, happy face and looked a very sincere man. They were not a great distance from each other - Howard was in Staffordshire and Marie in Nottinghamshire. But the most amazing aspect of their match was that Howard had written down that he had never had a girlfriend, just as Marie had revealed to me that she had also never had a serious boyfriend.

Well, maybe they could learn together, I thought. So the introduction was put forward to them both. For several months, all went quiet. If I don't hear anything at the beginning of an introduction I usually leave well alone which is what I did here. My clients know I am always there to help or advise but I never interfere. Then out of the blue Howard telephoned me one day and said that he and Marie would very much like me to visit them both preferably at his house. It was February 1999 and he said they really would like me to come on Valentine's Day, if that was possible. I thought that things must be going well if I was asked to meet them together but had no idea as to the extent of the relationship.

I arrived at Howard's home in the early afternoon to be greeted at the farm gate by two small dogs, smothered in long fur, who were quite yappy but seemed friendly enough. I left the car on the drive and walked up to the bungalow, a small, neat home with a few farm buildings around it. The door opened as I put up my hand to knock revealing two of the friendliest looking people I've ever encountered. Smiles from both as wide and happy as you could get and both exuded a warmth that seemed to envelope me instantly.

They ushered me into their cosy little home and settled into a comfy armchair. The signs looked good, I thought. Maybe I've cracked it again here. After they had both sat down on the settee opposite me we started to chat about various things. It was obviously going to take a while for them to come to the point of why they had asked me to visit so I asked them to tell me how they felt about my bureau and matchmaking and whether it had worked for them.

Howard then started to tell me that he had actually written off for my brochure about seventeen years previously and never, in all that time, had he found the courage to go through with joining. It completely staggered me that it had taken so much time to actually decide to join. "You just do not know what goes through people's minds," I thought. So then I asked them both to tell me what had finally pushed them to get in touch with me in the end.

Howard said that the last straw that actually made him fill in my form was that he had written to Voice Personnel, yet again, in the papers and was so sick of being let down. The last lady he had contacted he had met just once in a car park when she was on her way home. They had arranged to meet at a theatre again but she didn't turn up and then he couldn't get her on the telephone. Her daughter used to answer the phone saying to Howard, "Me mam isn't in." He felt despondent as this went on for about six weeks.

He continued with a marked sadness in his tone. "Anyway, I felt so desperate that I decided from now on I was going through a third party. I was so hurt and disappointed." The rejection came through in his voice. How little we all realise, I thought, how massive the hurt to someone can be, when we dismiss them so easily.

He continued, "I was off work for a while after that with a bad back pain (he worked part time from his small farm as a driver for a local company). With being off work I'd go for days upon days without actually seeing anybody. I used to go up to town, and the girls at the checkout in the supermarket wouldn't speak. You would just get your food, pay your money and come back out again, and you could actually return home without having had a conversation with anyone. The only person who would speak to me was the one at the chip shop. Well I wasn't supposed to have fish and chips really but I was getting to the stage where, if I wanted to talk to somebody for a few minutes, I'd got to go and buy a packet of chips and perhaps throw them away again when I got home. I just wanted so much to speak to someone. That was about the only hope I had of having anyone to talk to."

The total despondency of that time in his life showed so obviously in his face that I wanted to get up and comfort him, but he went on to say, "Christmas came and for three days I never saw a soul let alone spoke to anyone. When I was doing my driving job I never came across female company much at all. It's such male-orientated work when you're driving. Usually I was taking cement onto building sites. It's all men all the time."

Then Howard said, "I knew the lady I was looking for was sitting at home somewhere by herself just like me. I knew I wouldn't find her in a pub or anything like that. I used to go to the theatre occasionally but it was always on my own and you could go there and come back again without speaking to anybody. People would be in groups or couples and I would never want to push my company on anyone who did not want it. Even if you see a woman in a group with other lady friends, you don't know if they've got a partner or not. I always found it an impossible situation."

Marie said, "People who are not in a situation like Howard don't realise, do they, this state of absolute loneliness. And of course Howard was not the only one. I was doing similar things over in the next county because I was so lonely. One thing we both found out was that for years we have kept the radio on throughout the night. You can't stand the continual silence so with a radio on at least you feel you have someone with you in the night."

Howard continued, "I'd seen your adverts in the papers. I think it used to be in the British Farmer, or one of the other farming papers. But then I would think to myself, well no one would ever want to be with me, so I would never dare approach you. I suppose I've got a terrible inferiority complex. I thought over the years that I wasn't worth anything to anybody. I felt I'd never had anything else but rejection all my life, even as a child. I've been approaching ladies for a date since before I was twenty, but I went for ten or thirteen years without even asking anybody out because I couldn't stand being constantly rejected. Anyway, I was so disappointed with how I could hardly ever get a date with the newspaper adverts that I really had decided I wouldn't bother with them again. I'll go to Mrs Warrens Bureau - a third party, so I'll know where I stand."

"In my dreams I'd always wanted to meet a nurse. Maybe it's because they are caring people and a nurse wouldn't mock you or easily reject you because she would understand the hurt. When the paperwork came on Marie and I saw she was a nurse, I was overwhelmed, and I have to admit I cried." His face showed to me then, the utter disbelief that she had come into his life.

I asked Marie how she had come to join the Bureau and she admitted that it was through her vet's practice. "They insisted - the vets and all the nurses - that I got in touch with you because they thought my life was being wasted. They got all the papers for me and filled everything out and said to me 'sign here.' It's taken me a lifetime to trust anyone as I lost all my confidence for years and years. I couldn't seem to regain my self esteem and I just threw myself into my career and then, of course, first my mother and then my father became ill and I had to look after them. I loved them both so much I just wish they could have met Howard. I know my dad would have got on with him. Afterwards, when I was completely alone, I just got more and more depressed. Then my dog died and I really went into a decline. So I decided to finish work as a midwifery sister."

Howard started to say, "You know the similarities in our lives before we met are immense. Although they're different situations the same emotions are involved so we do understand what each other has gone through." Marie then put her arm through Howard's as they sat on the sofa together and she said, "My confidence has been restored by this wonderful man."

Out of the blue Howard said to me, "You know you fixed up my cousin Diane's daughter to a man called Malcolm, an agricultural engineer. I used to deliberately ring Diane and she said to me one night, "Howard, why don't you join Mrs Warren's Bureau?' It stuck in my mind and I couldn't think of a reason why not and those words rung in my ears."

I asked Howard to tell me a little about his earlier life. He told me that he'd bought this land off his dad before he sold it with the main farm. So at last he'd got something which was his own, independent and separate from the family. He built this small bungalow. He described how he had always reared livestock but started to go lorry driving to bring in a guaranteed income. As I looked around I could see that the bungalow was quite new. It had glorious views on the one side leading down to a lake and the undulating countryside of North Staffordshire on the other. His acreage was small but Howard was never going to be into big time farming and he said he was happy that way. Through the large picture window we could see about twenty good, strong looking bullocks.

I asked them both what their first impressions were when they had started speaking on the phone to each other. Marie told me that when Howard first telephoned her she immediately thought what a lovely, trusting and sincere voice he had. They didn't meet straight away but made quite a few phone calls over several weeks.

For their first meeting, Howard suggested Carsington Reservoir, a lake and leisure complex half way between them both. They started giggling and Howard explained "We were in a mess really, because there are about a thousand car park spaces there, you see, and I got the last one. It was Easter weekend so about a million other people were there that afternoon."

Mocking themselves with great hilarity for choosing such a silly day with half the population of the Midlands there as well, Marie continued the story of how she had to keep driving round all the car parks. She had already walked round all the cars but could not see his registration number. In any case, apparently he'd got that wrong anyway! They both laughed at the ridiculous situation that they had got into and we agreed it was a miracle they ever even met.

Howard thought the only thing he could do was sit in his car and wait and Marie said that she just kept riding round all the car parks until she eventually saw a red Volvo. A man got out but she couldn't really look at him as she still hadn't found anywhere to park. Eventually they both stopped and Howard walked over to her and suggested that she should follow him to the village of Tissington. Apparently he hadn't even asked her if she was Marie! But the problem now was that they were holding all the traffic up. They both laughed uproariously again at the memory and Marie admitted that she hadn't got a clue where she was driving when she started to follow Howard that afternoon.

Howard said, "The first words she said to me when we eventually parked up were that I was handsome - can you believe that? Me handsome! No one had ever in the whole of my life told me that before. We were holding hands within two minutes. It was lovely. We found a tearoom and I think I fell in love with her while we were having a cup of tea and I thought to myself that I'm not going to let this one slip through the net."

They snuggled up to each other and literally gazed into each other's eyes and you could tell that they were truly and deeply in love, just like a couple of teenagers.

Marie then told me she had cried all the way home because she thought Howard wouldn't want to see her again. She described how much she liked him and she knew she could love him because he was sincere and he was just the type of person that she wanted to love.

As they talked to me there was so much emotion at this point, again particularly from Marie. Her arm went through his and she touched him gently on the cheek, maybe to confirm that all this was taking place and Howard was real.

Howard said, "We spoke on the phone again and arranged to meet up in the centre of Ashbourne. Marie had suggested we meet in the car park in the middle of town. Well, I waited for three hours against that stone statue. I kept buying car parking tickets but then I decided this was no good so I drove over to where she lived in Nottinghamshire. It was a bit of a struggle because I didn't know the way. Anyway, I did manage to get there eventually. It took about half as many miles again, but I did get there."

"When he arrived," said Marie, "I was in tears because I'd just got back from driving all around Ashbourne and I hadn't seen Howard at all and thought he just hadn't bothered to turn up. Then I couldn't believe that he would put himself out enough to drive all that way to come to see me! I was overwhelmed. Of course that was the first time that we had been able to relax and then really get to know each other. It was wonderful. For the first time in my life it seemed that someone wanted me and wanted me for myself, not just for what I could do for them."

Howard asked Marie to stay for a weekend but Marie couldn't as she had no one to look after her dogs. She couldn't really leave her home for more than a couple of hours.

"I'd got eight dogs at the time. You see, I'd taken in stray dogs to compensate for my loneliness. I finished up, I suppose, being a prisoner in my home and I didn't realise that until Howard pointed it out to me. One dog was paranoid about Howard when he came. He wouldn't leave him and was constantly jumping up at him and barking. Some of them were very jealous of him coming onto the scene. Howard told me that I'd been so good to them, that I'd reared them and saved them from the needle. Then he said that they'd now grown up and needed homes of their own. I listened to every word he said because I know when somebody's talking common sense and I knew he was telling me the truth. I never intended keeping all the dogs anyway so I managed to find homes for all of them except the two here today."

They both laughed so much at this predicament and continued to tell me that Marie then visited Howard's farm and not only did she fall in love with its owner but was immediately totally smitten with the little house and the surrounding countryside.

When Howard went to stay for his first weekend at Marie's it was the first time he'd stayed away from his home since he was about fifteen or sixteen. "I had the biggest job to persuade myself to get in the car and come away from here. It took an hour or two. I'd got my bags packed but I just couldn't get used to not being here. I checked all the doors, windows and plugs two or three times and made sure I'd locked up and checked I had everything and even then I found it very difficult. It was only sheer determination to achieve what I wanted, to love and make a life with Marie and get rid forever of the sheer loneliness and despair, that got me through the door."

"I wanted to keep the love I had for Marie to myself for a while. I suppose I was worried it would all fall through but Marie wanted me to ring my mother up. I said, "I've got a new friend," and she said, "What's his name?" I don't know whether she was thinking I'd got a boyfriend or what? That's the danger when you're single at our age - everybody thinks that you're gay. Well I only told one person after that and that was Edgar and it was a complete surprise to him. He used to work for my dad before I was born. I knew he wouldn't be able to contain himself. I knew I didn't have to tell anybody else. I just said to him, "Don't tell anybody," and that sealed it. Edgar would tell everybody!"

Both then explained that once Marie had found good homes for the dogs she would come over and spend a few days with Howard then go home and both of them would be totally miserable. One day Howard put his foot down and said he did not want her to be living by herself anymore so she moved in.

"The biggest excitement the neighbours had was the day a new double bed arrived at my front door. They all got to know about it as the furniture men could not find the farm and asked at one or two other farms down the road for directions. So news of the arrival of the double bed spread like wildfire around the locality within a few hours," Howard proudly exclaimed.

He then said, "Sometimes, when I'm outside and I look back at this bungalow, I can't believe the gem I've got inside. Before I met Marie I used to be up the fields and I'd walk back down to the bungalow, perhaps it'd be dark and there'd be no light on or the curtains would be open and there'd be no-one moving about, and it looked empty and dead. I used to sort of despair with the loneliness and weariness. It was terrible. I used to look through my photograph album virtually every day for companionship."

But now life has changed so much and they have found perfect contentment in each other. "It's so beautiful here in the countryside," Marie said. "Even to see a mouse running around or the hares in the field or the change of the seasons. You know we're both crazy about the English countryside. We don't need foreign holidays at all because we don't feel we need to escape especially now we've got each other. Everything we need is here."

Marie said that hiding under that quiet exterior is the kindest, loveliest man you would wish to meet and told me that no one knew that he wrote poetry and had a wicked sense of humour. She explained that sometimes she has to beg him to stop telling jokes and imitating people as she just can't stop laughing."

Howard next spoke about how much his life had changed. "One day we went with some friends of Marie to a farm where a Lancaster Bomber was being rebuilt. All the engines were running and we had a ride in it. The same friends then took us to the coast that day and I realised that it's the first time I've been to the coast for about thirty five years. The last time I remember seeing the sea was on a daytrip to Blackpool when I was about twenty one."

Marie said " The greatest sadness I have is that we did not both come to you when we were much younger because I would so much like to have had Howard's children and now it's too late. I sometimes try to imagine what they would have been like. If we could encourage other single people to do the same as we have done it would be so good because loneliness is by far the most terrible thing that ever happens to anyone."

I said to both of them, "It seems to me, sitting here and listening to you, what a sensible, down to earth couple you are. Out of the blue, without ever having to handle emotional aspects of a relationship, there you are at the helm of this ship steering things so well."

Howard then became quite serious and said, "We want you to be the first to know, Pat, as it is all through you, that today with you by our side we would like to get engaged."

Wow, I thought, this is quite something. This is the stuff that fairy tales are made of and before I could continue with my thoughts Howard had got out of his pocket a little box. He opened it and took out a pretty diamond ring and, turning to Marie and holding her hand, he said to her, "You are everything in the world to me. I cannot imagine my life without you now or ever," and with that he slipped the ring onto the third finger of her left hand and said, "You were worth waiting thirty years for."

The kiss that followed was filled with such love and devotion my heart nearly burst with joy at watching and witnessing the scene on Valentine's Day 1999.

One year on, as I dozed in the chair thinking about the story of Marie and Howard on Valentine's Day 2000, I realised I could not slumber anymore and would have to get a move on. I showered and changed from my smelly farm clothes to a sober suit more appropriate for an office interview with the BBC.

I was asked in the BBC interview all about the work I do connected with the office and then, while the film crew had some breakfast, I changed into my wedding outfit. The TV crew filmed me as I was doing my hair and putting on my wedding hat. Then it was a dash for them to go over to set up their cameras ready for the wedding.

I was due to arrive at Howard's farm a short while before Marie was due to set off. After being up all night it was a good job that I had to drive through the Staffordshire moorlands. With the windows down the fresh air certainly woke me up.

Marie was very excited and had just finished getting ready. She was full of laughter as she always is but, as with all brides, quite awe struck at what she was about to do. She wore a lovely misty pastel green and cream dress with a cream coat, a big picture hat made in the beautiful colours of her dress, and an exquisite bouquet of pastel mint, lemon and cream. She looked radiant and I told her so. Throughout the time she was getting ready she had had a TV news crew filming the beginning of her special day.

Howard seemed be nowhere around but I believe he was at the farmhouse to the west. The farmer to the east arrived in his splendidly ribbon bedecked car to take Marie to her wedding service. It was to be a real little country wedding and we all set off for the ceremony with

Marie's film crew dashing off beforehand. Excitement mounted because when we reached our destination the police had closed the road as there were so many reporters and TV crews around.

The music 'The Power of Love' was played at the beginning of the ceremony and by the end there wasn't a dry eye in the house. Even the hardened TV and newspaper reporters were emotional as they filmed them coming out as man and wife. A man came up to me on the pavement and said "Is it really true that Howard is getting married here today? Well, I never! I was told in town this morning that this was happening but I couldn't believe it so I had to come and see for myself." At that point Marie and Howard appeared, being showered with confetti, looking radiantly happy.

The TV crew then rushed away as they wanted to show the wedding on the lunch time Valentine's Day news programmes. We all drove to the reception several miles away into the countryside. It's always the same when I attend any wedding receptions. I always get the feeling they really don't know where to put me. On which side, bride or bridegroom, should I sit? Who do I sit by? I know when couples invite me they tend to feel I should have quite a high priority seat but where? The etiquette books don't yet cater for someone like me. Once at a wedding in East Anglia I was placed next to a Bishop so that was, I suppose, quite prestigious. Mostly I seem to be seated next to a special aunt but this time I was seated next to Howard's eldest brother and sister in law.

He said to me, "It's quite incredible. I still can't believe that it's our Howard here today with all these TV film crews and newspapers. He's always been so very quiet all his life. We knew nothing at all about this romance, you know, until just over a month before they got engaged. Then this one Saturday night I was having a bath and my wife appeared with a newspaper." His wife took over the tale. "I always read the Sentinel of a Saturday night and as I was glancing through I started to read a letter a couple had sent in. I read who it was from, and thought, "I'm misreading this. I'll have to go and get my glasses." When I put my glasses on, it read the same. It was from Howard telling about his love for this lady. I was speechless. I had to go straight up to Edward to show him and we just could not take it in." I smiled to myself as they were telling me all this and thought how wonderful that life can still be full of surprises.

The reception went beautifully. Everyone had a good time and Marie and Howard left with wishes of so much goodwill and laughter. They didn't have a honeymoon. They said they just wanted to be in their home together and look after the twin goats that had been born that morning on the farm.

On Valentine's Day 2001, one year to the day after their wedding, John and I paid Marie and Howard another visit. This time it was to attend a very small but sincerely felt blessing of their marriage service in their small parish church.

12
A Tall Order

I can think of nothing more annoying when you join an Introduction Agency than having someone constantly bombarding you with advice and pushing their own feelings and approach to life onto you when you don't need it and don't want it. I aim not to give advice until it is asked for and I always try to work to that philosophy. However, I do know that many people are very apprehensive and may be a little confused about how to meet someone through an agency, especially shy retiring people who lead rural lives. City dwellers are mostly used to communicating on many levels, but for that quiet country person who does not mix with many people and possibly does not have a lot of friends their own age it can all seem a daunting prospect. In the centre pages of the Bureau brochure I have written down advice which a Bureau member can digest and take on board if they want to. In it I outline methods of getting to know each other. I warn against trying to rush into a relationship and encourage my clients to have a positive outlook towards their eventual success.

Romance will come along 'when you least expect it.' That is a phrase that I definitely believe in. One of the most curious occurrences is that a Bureau member will come for an interview. They will tell me how they have been trying to meet someone special for years and years. They then say, "Now I've joined you everything will be alright. I'm sure you'll find me someone." This is very unnerving because, although it's good that they have faith in the Bureau, I worry that they will think all their woes in life will now be solved. However, what has happened so many times is that a few weeks after that person has gone home, I get a call from them. Embarrassed, they inform me that in the last week or two, since they joined the Bureau, they have amazingly met someone without my help and the friendship seems to be leading into quite a special relationship. They can't believe it and certainly can't understand how they can go for years never developing a relationship but, as soon as they put themselves into my hands, they do.

Well, I think that is the essence of it all. Once they have done something positive such as joining The Bureau, in their minds they say, "Right, that's fixed and done. There is no need for me to try any more. The Bureau is going to do everything for me in the romantic department," and they relax. By being relaxed and giving off an aura of not desperately seeking a mate, all occasional meetings with other people are considerably more stress free. They do not try because there is no need to try. The Bureau is going to do it all for them. With this more relaxed attitude romance seems to come through the door when you least expect it.

One of the great things about dealing with different sorts and types of people in the office is that you can get into the most intriguing conversations 'when you least expect it.' Something that I am always 'least expecting,' but getting more of, are calls from gay men and women who want to know if I can help them. I'd like to able to say I can help anyone at all who lives in the countryside no matter what their orientation but at the moment I just cannot help this minority group because that is exactly what it is. There are so few people who approach me with this issue that even if I did form a sub-section of my main register, their choice with me would be so small and a gay person needs to have as much choice as any heterosexual person. I do advise them, however to join an agency called Significant Others which has a good reputation in the introduction industry.

How life changes! Twenty years ago I would never have had calls from gay people but of course it is good that society is so much more open.

As we all know women's expectations have changed dramatically over the years. I am asked so often by a man to find 'someone just like my mother.' To which my reply is there will never be anyone the same as your mother and nowadays many women want a completely different lifestyle; independence, an ability to make decisions rather than depend on their husband to do all that for them and the desire to make a financial contribution to the family, usually by going off the farm to work. So the stereotyped farmer's wife who stays at home all day baking bread and making jam, with masses of children running at her feet and chickens roaming around just outside the farmhouse door, is becoming less of a reality.

Of course I'm in favour of women having greater choices in life. But sometimes I do wonder if women actually enjoy a greater quality of life when all they are doing day in, day out is working away from home and juggling their lives as mothers, wives and income providers, trying to keep all the balls up in the air but not knowing when one will fall.

When discussing the changing make-up of human society I am at times asked about my feelings on marriage in the future. Well, really who can say? Maybe things will reverse and go back to marriage becoming more popular, but possibly not. I think that more and more people will be reluctant to enter into the implications of marriage without trying it out first and the old fashioned pattern of engagement, marriage and then living together will be unusual.

One thing I have found with some modern women is that they don't try to be women at all. They think it is quite wrong to be feminine. Little do they realise that one of the main criteria a man will ask me about a woman is if she is feminine. Of course I can be totally wrong at times. Someone might ask me, "What do you think I should wear on my first date." I'll say, "Maybe a skirt would be good," and they will reply, "Never, I always wear trousers." Sometimes introductions like that go wonderfully well and I certainly am put in my place for being so sceptical.

Of course I have been proved wrong many times. There are actually no hard and fast rules because as soon as you set these down, human nature comes along and gladly throws them aside. Sometimes I'm reluctant to accept a person onto the register. I would never feel this lack of enthusiasm because of someone being unattractive physically, but I can recall instances when I have thought a person was so very miserable or had what I thought the wrong attitude. Sometimes life has given me a bit of a jolt in these circumstances and I can remember two particular occasions and clients who I thought would not easily form attachments. And yet, their first introductions proved absolutely successful.

One lady who I interviewed was a profoundly miserable person with no smile or humour and little or no warmth in her at all. Within weeks of giving her the first introduction the man let me know he was deliriously in love with her and was going to ask her to marry him. She didn't bother to phone me but he has always kept in touch and I believe they are still happily married. Isn't it amazing?

The second instance was a very masculine woman who came for an interview. In fact, when she walked in, had I not received her registration form prior to her coming, I would not have known if she was a man or woman. She was incredibly well educated and I thought this would daunt most of the men on my register. Yet the first introduction proved blissfully successful, instantly. Although they aren't yet married I have had letters from both him and her declaring their devotion and love for each other.

When this happens I concede that I don't know everything and these instances certainly put me in my place and teach me a thing or two. Once again I bow down and pay homage to the incredible power of human nature.

The power of the human spirit was certainly put to the test in the agricultural world in the early spring of 2001 when Foot and Mouth

Disease was diagnosed in some parts of the country. Some Bureau members who were in the middle of the whole awful business went completely quiet for weeks. They couldn't venture off their farms as their stock had been killed and they afterwards told me they were in such absolute shock that they couldn't raise their heads or some even their bodies to look forward to another day. Some affected by Foot and Mouth told me that they literally just went to bed for days. They couldn't take in the fact that all their animals had actually been culled, especially if the animals did not have the disease but were just contacts. Of course the men on my register were usually living by themselves with no wife or girlfriend to lean on and get support from. To some I did become that much needed crutch and sometimes grown men would weep uncontrollably down the phone. I would just listen and then try very hard to get them to look to a future. I felt at least I was able to do my little bit to help in this whole dreadful episode of farm life.

Gradually as the year progressed from those dreadful early days in February and March of that year, things began to get a little back to normal. Life had to go on. Foot and Mouth carried on all summer but we all tried to develop an optimistic outlook on life.

Springtime, for me, always brings with it such hope for the year ahead and I'm sure this sentiment is true for most people. I seem to get up with great enthusiasm in comparison to the previous dark and dreary winter mornings and I have a definite 'spring' in my step, probably delighted to be up and doing my round of activities in the early morning sunshine. Although please don't visualize me too clearly jumping about or doing a May Day dance naked in the early morning dew. It would not be a pretty sight.

It was on one of these early spring days that I met up again with a couple who had joined the Bureau in the previous year.

Sarah was such a sincere person; full of passion for what she believed in but she exerted that enthusiasm with a calm and mellow nature. Before she came for an interview at the office she had obviously thought about the implications of joining the Bureau very seriously. She wrote me a letter saying:-

"I'm not a complicated person. From my early years I just wanted to continue farming into my adult life. I am a farmer's daughter so I know what the life is like. I am quite strong and dependable workwise and able to work through problems and be strong throughout difficult days. I would just like to get on with jobs that need doing and build something good with a special person. I realised two to three years ago that I was never going to settle outside farming."

She continued by writing, "Other people have told me that this is a naive and a romantic idea and have said to me that one day I will grow up. If my dreams were to come true the falling in love bit would be to a kind and warm-hearted man, a bit boyish and tall. He would be an easygoing person who could see the funny side of everything. He would not be over ambitious. He would be a man who smiled often and had kind eyes. He would respect people and all their differences. I would like to be able to laugh easily with him at things that happen in day-to-day life. He would be very practical and not too serious. He would possibly have a small farm, which he loved and this would be his world and he would be content with it and with the local area. He would work hard and he would be a person who could see the greater picture of life and humanity in this world. He would be open-minded and he would not be driven to wanting a high material lifestyle or wanting to travel all over the place. I imagine a basic farmhouse that is very practical - not showy but cosy. Knowing me I would possibly be trying to get a small farm venture off the ground. It would be something like chickens and eggs. It would not be a big business. I would just basically love this life."

When she appeared at the Bureau office I noticed how attractive she was, both physically and in her character. Sarah would deny this straight away. She was so natural looking. She did not wear excessive make up and she dressed casually. She had no need for falseness or flouncy attire at all to enhance her looks. Her complexion and athletic slimness radiated good health and fitness. She was tall, had short auburn hair, a slim frame and was then in her early thirties.

She was born and brought up on a small farm in Kent. The farm was taken over by the family in the 1930s. Her childhood was remembered as quite idyllic. It was relaxed and easygoing but at the same time emphasis was put on education, especially for her as it was assumed she would not come into the farm. Sarah obtained four 'A' levels and then studied to become an architect. After qualifying she worked in various capacities; working in third world countries and in urban and city projects. Although she enjoyed designing she never felt comfortable with the work and has known for many years that her real joy was agriculture. She was basically a very practical, down to earth woman who was never happier than when muddy and dirty and involved with livestock or growing things. After working in Scotland for a while she went back to the family farm to help them during a difficult period.

One of her interests, she told me at the interview, was France. She loved the country and went out there as often as she could. She then said that if she did not meet someone special in the near future she would go out there to live permanently. Just work around different farms maybe. At the moment she was learning French.

Sarah had never married. She was a friendly, outgoing person who got on well with people and was quite intuitive towards others. She loved people with 'character.' She was, however, very pessimistic and said to me, "You will never find someone for me. Maybe you should not even put me on your register."

Out of the blue William became a member of the Bureau. He seemed to have strength in his character and a very pleasant and friendly manner. At our first meeting he was slightly shy but after five or so minutes into the Interview he started to relax and be himself.

William was in his thirties and six feet two inches in height. He was well built with broad shoulders, short brown hair and a great smile. He dressed mostly casually and was certainly attractive in appearance.

William's home was in Oxfordshire and his parents were both from farming families going back generations and had always farmed. Throughout the years a large family farm was built up. Sadly William's mother died in early 2001. William was educated at the local state school. He did not pursue further education. His main wish was to go into farming as soon as he could. Therefore, at sixteen years of age, he went into the farm with his father and worked exceedingly hard for a number of years. They expanded the business, renting more land and worked long and punishing hours but he was determined to succeed. On reflection, he said that he had learnt that work, year in and year out, should not be the most important aspect of life.

In his teens he joined the YFC and attended for a number of years. He entered into all the social life and enjoyed this considerably. William had had a few girlfriends (not many) but did have one important relationship. After five years she realized she wanted to go back home to Australia and it seemed very difficult for William to follow her. So they realised their relationship was not meant to last and separated amicably.

William came across as being very hard working. In his twenties he worked around New Zealand and Australia for a while in various jobs on farms. On returning home he started to breed his own stock and rent his own land. Throughout the next ten years he built up a reputation for having really good stock and this has been reflected in the prices obtained for them at the top end of the market. He has always enjoyed showing his pedigree beef cattle.

He went on to tell me at the interview that he would very much like to farm completely on his own account and had decided that the best chance to do that would be to farm in France. He had been thinking about this for several years since farming had become more difficult in this country, especially without a farm of his own. He commented on how well young farmers are treated in France and was adamant that this would be the best move for him.

He had been to France twice looking at farms and had raised revenue through selling his herd of pedigree cattle to another farmer who is re-stocking after Foot and Mouth. With the financial means now available he would like to purchase a French farm (with a mortgage) and develop a good business. He was also doing a six-month course in learning French.

He admitted to desperately loving the land and a truly rural way of life. William's interests were all country orientated. He loved open spaces and he enjoyed riding out with the local hunt. He took his nephew fishing and went rabbiting and really enjoyed going to 'game fairs' and 'country shows.' He played hockey for the YFC and for many years played rugby. He lived in a cottage close to the family farm but about three quarters of a mile down a track surrounded by foxes, owls, and all the wildlife you could wish for. The simple things in life meant a great deal to him.

His love of wildlife and animals was so great that if his farming was at some time in the future not successful he could imagine working in something like a wild life park although he clearly did not wish that to happen. He told me that farming was and always would be his life.

I knew by getting to know him well that he had determination and an ability to get what he wanted. This 'grit' was softened by his easygoing temperament. He was a fair and straightforward man, treating people well, never losing friends and having high principles in all that he did.

William said he would like to meet a lady who would understand farming. It would be nice if, when settled in France, he had somebody by his side. He could see a wife developing her own business venture. However, it would be great if she understood the complexities and issues to do with farming and therefore he could share concerns and decisions with her. "To have support in my farming life would be wonderful and someone who was versatile and adaptable would be great," he said.

He concluded the interview with, "And I would like to have children one day. Do you think you can work miracles and find this lady? I've only got four months before I go to France."

"Wow! That's a tall order," I said but sometimes dreams do come true. You never know and you should never give up.

13

Come Live with Me and be My Love.......

Little did William know that I had Sarah in mind all the time. My second meeting with Sarah was three months after she first met William. I said, "Tell me Sarah. You told me it was best not to put you on my register. Why was that?"

She said, "Because I thought the type of person I knew I would be happy with did not exist."

"When you got my first letter about William what did you think?"

"Well," Sarah said, "Before I started reading it I said to myself that I had already made up my mind, I was going to France. Maybe he is nice but then, as I kept reading his profile, I thought, he really did sound very nice.

Then when I read that he wanted to farm in France I thought it was a complete wind up. I seriously thought that someone was playing a joke on me. I just never thought I would meet someone who wanted to do exactly the same as I wanted. My friends are wind up merchants and they knew I wanted to farm in France so I thought it was them, putting the letter together. Then I thought that they could not do that. They could not persuade you to play tricks and it was definitely your headed paper. I remember sitting in your office when I said I wanted to farm and told you all about my perfect partner. I remember mentioning how I loved France.

You had even said, 'Blimey, that's a tall order,' but maybe you say it to others as well."

Sarah continued, "So I knew I had left you with a hard task. I even remember saying I would like to meet some one who had a big smile. On William's profile you mentioned a big smile, a great sense of humour and very down to earth. I truly thought it was a wind up."

Sarah then went on to explain, "I could not believe what he said to me the first time we met. He just sat there and said everything that I had been thinking for so long about farming.

When we first met there were no worries at all. It was like meeting an old friend. We were so relaxed. There was never a moment when I thought Oh! My God what am I going to say now? We had so much to talk about; issues important to us, not the usual mention of hobbies and holidays. We were straight in there talking about farming and on exactly the same wavelength. We did it automatically and he was so easygoing. I had felt so isolated because none of my friends seemed to understand how I felt about the farming situation.

I knew they thought I was a bit daft. All the time I was told by them that it was so romantic, that it would never happen. 'Get real,' they told me.

I decided beforehand that I did not want to imagine too much about William's appearance. I switched off I suppose. It was because I did not want to make pre-judgements. That is why I did not want photos. A photo is just a still and a person is full of expression and character. I remember meeting a 'lumber jack' type of person who thrilled me on the outside but he turned out to be a weak willed computer buff. It is great that he is tall and that he likes tall girls and likes someone a bit older than himself as I'm just over a year older. When I read his profile I thought, 'pull the other one,' this sort of person, the sort I have in my dreams, does not really exist.

I felt a spark between us as soon as we met. I knew we would be more than just friends. I did not let on, of course. We went to the zoo. I think I was a bit concerned about animals in cages. I was a bit on edge. It just did not seem comfortable. He also said that he was not over keen about animals in cages. Without me prodding him he said he was not into zoos and that he didn't think it right for the animals. We met at eleven o'clock then we had lunch at the zoo and he left at about four pm.

When we parted I still could not believe it. He asked if I wanted to meet again. I wanted to say, 'You've found your person to go to France with.' What I actually said was, 'I think you should meet a few more girls as well as me and if you don't find someone better then come back to me.'

I could see he was looking worried and anxious as I said this. He said he didn't think he wanted to meet anyone else and wanted to meet me again. So we just left it at that. He tried to give me a little hug but I ducked away from him. I am so shy and I know I give the wrong impression when I do things like that.

He rang me up on the Saturday two days after that first meeting and I was really pleased to hear from him. We decided not to speak until the next Tuesday and it felt like years away. So I rang him up early as I thought I must show him a bit of heart as I do hide my feelings. I said to him Tuesday seems such a long way away. He said he was so pleased to hear from me but he was so tired. I thought, 'Well, it seems he is not interested in me,' and he said he would ring me the next day.

When the next day came he phoned my mobile and asked if I had a landline phone nearby. I was so pleased to hear from him. I told him the phone number and ran over to the farm shop telephone. As I was waiting for him to ring back my heart started to pound. I really thought he would say he had made a mistake.

He opened the conversation by saying, 'It has seemed such a long time to wait to talk to you.' I made a deafening sigh. 'Thank goodness,' I thought."

I interrupted Sarah's narrative and commented that it was incredible that they had met only once and just could not wait to be together. Sarah agreed.

"I really wanted him to come to my place," she said. "I wanted him to see the farm and the life I was leading. The problem was I was busy with the farm shop as it was virtually Christmas week, so he suggested he would visit me there.

I was waiting for him outside the farm shop when he arrived. We had a good walk around the farm and he was really very interested and he chatted to the others on the farm. I wanted him to meet my father and as we were walking around we just bumped into him; he was trying to mend a tractor. They had a chat about tractors and other such things and straight away they got on well. He called my dad a 'good old boy.' I was pleased that he saw me as me working on a farm. It was good because afterwards when I talked about the farm he understood all that I was going on about.

We looked around the farm a bit more and I worked up until lunchtime. I had to pack up some produce for market the next day and he helped me do that and move some stakes. We both prefer to be working. In the early evening we drove back to where I live. It's a very old farmhouse. I had cooked a meal in the slow oven and so I was able to prepare it quickly. I lit a fire and we chatted around the fireside and he told me quite a lot more about his life."

I asked Sarah what they mostly talked about. Sarah said, "Well, it was a real in depth talk. William said, "We get on very well - we should make a go of it." As he said this I could tell he was slightly nervous. I was just smiling at him. I suppose I made him work hard at this little speech. He was fidgeting but with a smile on his face. He was saying that we like this and we like that in common and he thought we had a future together. Then he said, "Don't be too worried. I am not asking you to marry me straight away you know."

I just laughed at him. Everything he said I was agreeing with and nodding but did not say much. I am much better at writing and I'd written him a nice card that day. It said I thought the world of him. And I thanked him for spending the time with me. William said that he felt so relaxed with me and that I made him feel so happy. He then asked 'Do I get a kiss this time?' I was still a bit shy so we had a little hug but he had hurt his ribs so I said I must be careful with him and there was no kiss.

Christmas came and I stayed with some friends a few counties away. Before I met William I thought I would want to be alone at this time. I really had got into such a despondent state in the previous months. Now I was eager to see all my friends. I could have spent Christmas with William but as this was the first Christmas for his family without their mother I thought it right for him to spend it with his sister. We did ring each other up on Christmas Day, though.

After Christmas William wanted to cook a meal using a turkey he had in the freezer and he wanted all his family to come. He asked me to go along for this big family meal. There was also a farmers black tie event close to his home which he asked me to go to as well. Just before I went to his home for the first time I suggested that we should do something a bit different and so we decided to have a good walk around London and went up on the London Eye. It was different. It was not really our scene but it was interesting to see a different place and we had lovely day. The day before I had written him a letter in which I told him all my feelings for him and I gave it to him at the little café at the bottom of the London Eye. 'I'll get the coffees if you sit down and read it,' I insisted.

I explained that due to my shyness a man really has to chase me and the sledgehammer approach would be more effective in getting the first loving kiss. A friend did ask me if we had kissed yet and on hearing that we hadn't exclaimed 'Poor lad.' "Don't worry," I told her, "I will let him know that he has to take control of me in that area."

The next time we met I went to his cottage. I was so apprehensive that he was going to give this big party when I would meet his family for the first time. He cooked the turkey and I cooked the vegetables. It was instant teamwork. We had to cook for twelve people so we had to borrow some furniture. I was really nervous but they were such good fun. I was so pleased to meet them all and I could see how William fitted in. They were all genuine people.

We then went to the Farmers Ball. He had told all his friends about me so everyone knew about us and how we met. One of his brothers was great. He made me feel so welcome. I do love dancing and I was up there with all his mates and their partners. William told me I looked very smart and nice. He looked so handsome and I was so proud to be with him and it was great dancing with him. All the farmers know each other and we had some great laughs.

When the evening came to an end we walked out together - both well dressed- after such a fabulous evening. I reflected, "Life is great." If you had asked me to write down on paper the type of man I thought I needed to meet I would have described William."

Sarah did not remember that she had done this in a letter to me.

Sarah delayed the deadline she had set herself for going to France. "I was going off at the end of February and William had planned to go about April. Now we are going next week to spend a week in France. I speak a little French and William is learning."

The routine now is that Sarah works six days a week at the farm then she drives to William's cottage on Saturday night. When they go to France they have decided to go for a short time and then come back for a few weeks and afterwards leave for good.

Sarah said, "I did not want to set up a place on my own. I've seen women get very hard being on their own. I just wanted to be part of a couple, farming together. The government supports farming in France and they seem anxious to encourage the younger farmer to stay in the countryside."

I concluded my talk with Sarah by asking, "You came to me and said you wanted to meet a particular type of man. I think I have found him for you. Do you?"

Sarah replied, "He is just the person I would have made up in my wildest dreams. Even the 'earthly instincts' that I knew in my heart I so much wanted to find, are there. Yes," she said "Thank you."

When I spoke to William for the second time I asked him about the first occasion he came to the Bureau office. "Tell me," I said, "You came to see about finding a prospective wife to go with you to France. When you left my office did you go away hopeful?" William replied, "Well I really thought it would be months before I heard anything."

I asked him what he thought of Sarah's profile when I sent it. "Well first of all when I read it she looked very bright. She is very brainy you know but it's odd that she doesn't like the academic side of life. I am clever on the practical side but in theory I'm just average. I was a bit naughty because I left Sarah's profile on the side, at home and my brother actually read it by accident. He remarked that she looked a brainy girl and I told him that she was easygoing and down to earth.

"We got on so well straight away. She ended the evening by saying that I should meet other girls and if I didn't find anyone better then come back to her. I didn't want that."

I said to William, "I think sometimes when something good comes along that you have waited for so long it is not easy to recognise. You don't immediately put your hand out and grab it and I think that is what happened to Sarah."

He continued, "Well, I was determined to get a yes out of her. We laugh about it now. Of course she did agree to meet me again. I said to her, "I will lay my cards on the table. I'd be happy to settle down with you." We went to the local Farmers Ball. Everyone wanted to meet her. She had a lot of teasing but took it all well and she loved it. She got on so well with all my friends and she looked so lovely. I told her that and she blushed. Neither of us dress up very often, so it was good to see each other like that.

When we came out of the Ball, we'd had such a good time and she looked so beautiful I decided to take command of the situation. I put my arms around her and told her that now the time was right for our first real kiss.

That night I went and got a chain from my workshop and started fiddling about with it on my door. She asked me what I was doing. I told her I was just chaining up my bedroom door so she couldn't overpower me and have her wicked way." She collapsed with laughter knowing how shy and sexually reserved she had been with him throughout the previous weeks. By saying all this I suppose William had put her at ease and indicated that they had all the time in the world to explore this part of their relationship.

"So what are your plans now William?" I asked.

"As you know," William replied, "I've been planning for a long time to actually move permanently to France. I don't think we should purchase a farm with the money I have straight away. I'd rather wait a year, maybe, and work in the area to get an idea of the lie of the land. Of course Sarah was planning to go to France to work anywhere on a farm. Sarah is very good at French and far better than me. I can order food and do some conversation but not as good as Sarah. She is bright and she can help with the necessary paperwork in trying to get set up.

I know we will come across problems but I feel the two of us in our hearts really want a good life together. I really want to set up on my own and I've said to Sarah I really cannot be doing with arguments. The relationship I share with Sarah now is so different from any other relationships I've had. I have to say I think about her all day, now, and I find myself smiling when I think of something special she has said or done. Before, to tell you the truth, I could never understand why anyone wanted to get married. But I can see why, now that I know Sarah. She is a good, genuine lady; a rare breed and a real good country girl."

I said to William, "When you go to France it will be a bit like pioneering when people used to go to America."

"Yes, but I was thinking just a few months ago that I might have to do it on my own. At least now I have Sarah."

As I journeyed home from being with William my mind was full of excitement for them and the new life they had found together. But do they realise what hard work they have in front of them? It will be totally exhausting, seven days a week for a long time. No matter how much I thought of the difficulties that lay ahead of them my spirits would not be dampened by hard reality and I could not let go of the exhilaration and the pure romance of their life together.

14.
It Takes All Sorts.

March, April and May are the busiest months on a livestock farm. Most of the animals have been inside for the winter, maybe all of it if it has been a particularly severe time. Our dairy herd would have started to go inside at night throughout October, especially if the autumn was wet. By November they would be inside day and night. So, by spring, for virtually half the year, muck and slurry have been collecting and rising higher and higher in the sheds as each month passes.

The animals will go out into the fields as soon as the grass has grown enough to sustain them. Usually non-milking animals will be put out first followed by the dairy herd when the spring grass has really come on well. The grass will not start to grow until the weather has become considerably warmer, usually late April for us. The grass growing season on farms in lower altitudes and further south starts much earlier than it does for us. High up on our limestone plateau in the Peak District of Derbyshire we are always counting the days when we can stop feeding silage and the great day has come when the cows will go out.

It is such a joy to wake up on these spring mornings and hear the birds singing and see the sun shining, to feel a bit of warmth and to know that the days of summer are just around the corner. I know those living urban lives will also feel this elation but with farmers the expectation of summer is often the only thing that keeps them going throughout those cold, hard and very long winter months.

In March all the land will be tended with the aim that the grass will grow quickly. We put fertilizer on all the fields first then hope for a nice interlude of warm wet weather which will encourage it to take effect. This, combined with the muck that has been spread over the land in the winter months, should encourage the grass to grow. With a bit of luck if you were able to start all the spring work in March, all might have been completed by the end of April. All the buildings and muck stores are cleaned out. The muck is dumped in a huge heap ready to be spread on the fields in the dark, cold days of winter when the fields are hard through frost and will not be marked by the heavy spreaders.

Next comes the harrowing. Every field is travelled over by the tractor pulling the harrows which are like a double bed of metal spikes. This has the effect of ripping through the ground and breaking up the muck that could still be in large pieces deposited there throughout the previous year. Its purpose is to level any mole hills and generally to even out ground that has been poached or made uneven by the footsteps of cows.

Everywhere is then rolled with a cylindrical metal roller to flatten down the ground and make it even in any silage fields which will help to depress any foreign objects or stones that, if left on the surface, could get mixed up with and do considerable damage to expensive farm machinery.

As well as all this work the walls have to be mended around the fields. All the fields at Mere Farm are surrounded by dry stone walls built of limestone without cement. In the course of the winter gaps would have occurred, sometimes through frost dislodging the stones and sometimes through wildlife or cows from the previous year. Dry stonewalling is quite an art and it takes years of experience to complete a wall. John and all the men would work on the walls but our most skilled man is Harold. He has been our main 'waller' for twenty years and we would be getting him to do a bit here and there throughout the whole year. He has always been particularly good at circles and turns, which, when you think about it, must be so difficult to judge. It is a delight to see his skill when he has built a perfect circle of stone around a mere. There is one mere close to the house around which he has built a ten-foot wall. It is truly a work of art, all completed by Harold Bonsall.

Gates also have to be repaired. String, which invariably has started to hold some gates together by the end of the year, will be replaced by the proper hinges and fastenings. I am always incredulous at the number of gates farmers have that take ages to open and close because they are fastened with string, baler twine and other unusual attachments or they do not hang properly and it takes the strength of two men to drag them across the appropriate opening.

By the time all this spring work has been completed the dairy herd will be turned out for the first time since the previous winter. In the autumn when it starts to get cold, dreary and wet, the doors of their buildings are left open for them to choose if they want to come into their winter buildings or not. They really do choose the comfort of their sheds. Warm, away from the rain and on nice dry straw beds with plenty of silage to eat, who can blame them? However, when springtime arrives they are undoubtedly fed up with being confined and look out from those sheds at the sunshine and grass with longing. "How do you know they have such emotions?" I am asked.

I love watching those first few moments when the herd is let loose for the first time in April. When first let out they initially seem to freeze with incredulous amazement. They stand and sniff the air and then reality takes over as they realise that they are free. They start by running, jumping and dashing around with such merriment and delight. Their tails go up in the air and they tend to run all over the field, visiting every corner. Then they start grazing quickly as they cannot believe they have got all this wonderful lush spring grass to eat. The men, John and I always stop and watch their enjoyment for the first ten minutes, but they quickly settle down, and within half an hour they are contentedly grazing and look as if they have never had the interlude of winter housing.

While all this work is going on we are also lambing our sheep flock. John always seems to prepare well for the three weeks when this takes place and organises all the antenatal and postnatal pens for the ewes well in advance. This ensures that our time whilst in the lambing sheds is used constructively to actually help the new borns into the world and not constantly thinking about where they are all going to go once born.

Any sheep farmer will tell you that the worst aspect of lambing is the lack of sleep. This is because you have to be with them virtually twenty four hours a day. We try to organise the routine so that John takes over the lambing in the evening and throughout the night and one of the workmen is in the sheep sheds during the daytime. Ben and Sarah would also work with the sheep when they were younger. It was the first thing they would do after school and throughout the evening they would constantly be running over to the sheep shed and doing small lambing jobs. As they have got older, as with so many farmers' children, the novelty has worn off.

With all these jobs to do you seem hardly able to have time to draw breath. Everywhere, however, does start to look as if it has had a good wash and brush up. All the doors to the buildings are left open and it's so satisfying to walk around and feel as if the whole farm has been spring cleaned from top to bottom. There is even a distinctive earthy but non-mucky smell everywhere.

Silaging will not take place for us until the end of May or even the beginning of June if it is cold and we have had bad weather. So for a while, instead of the constant hustle and bustle, our everyday life assumes a more leisurely pace and we are in that lull between spring work finishing and silaging beginning.

There is one job, however, that John dreads. I truly think he would prefer to go out and silage a hundred acres than get that dreaded lawnmower out! He always has great difficulty in starting it up after the winter and I know to keep away from him every spring when he does this. It will never start first time, so we have an inquest into what is wrong. Nothing that I can add in sympathy will be gratefully accepted. In fact, most Mays in our early years of marriage would end up in a great argument, all because of the lawnmower and its temperamental ways. Now, with experience, I just keep out of the way.

I wish we had the young man living close to us who joined my Bureau only a short time ago. When he came for an interview he told me that when he was eleven years old, he was so determined that one day he would have his own business that he started a lawnmowing enterprise. At the tender age of twelve years he had developed forty-five different customers including corporate businesses such as the local banks and had bought seven new lawnmowers and was employing six youths to work for him. He sold the lawnmowers at sixteen years of age and started to develop his contracting enterprise. Now only fourteen years later he has a million pounds worth of machinery bought and paid for and a contracting business that employed many men throughout the year, working several thousand acres throughout the southern counties. He had done all this in spite of being dyslexic and having to employ much help with his bookwork. An attractive looking man who had worked very hard, he had now reached thirty and wanted to settle down. How I could have done with his lawnmowing skills over the years when, come what may, whatever you did or did not do, the blessed lawnmower would not start.

So on the occasions of the lawnmower coming out of the shed for the first time I keep well out of the way and retreat to the Bureau office. I sit quietly by myself sometimes and think about the infinite range of relationships I have witnessed from some of the saddest to those that have the most wonderful endings. Of course to get to those happy endings sometimes people have to learn very hard lessons.

Some of the saddest situations in recent years have involved women who are just over forty years of age. I did not come across this so much twenty years ago but I now have many women in this age bracket who come to me and, in all honesty, it can be very difficult to find introductions for them. Men of forty who have not married are eager to meet women in their thirties. It can still be a bit of an old fashioned world in that women of child bearing age are in great demand but as soon as they get towards the forties men, knowing that their child producing days are nearly over, will look the other way. So you have got men still pursuing the dreams that men have had for centuries, to meet a younger woman and have children. On the other hand you have women living the twentieth century dream of liberation and equality wishing to be independent and prove their worth to one and all.

Nearly all these women will have achieved a lot in their careers. They will often have a degree and right from university would have thought that they had to succeed professionally. Marriage might have been in the back of their minds but it would have been something for the distant future. The years would have gone by and although they might have met good eligible bachelors, they would have always thought there was plenty of time to find Mr Right and settle down. Getting towards forty all of a sudden they would hear their biological clock ticking, possibly for the very first time.

Women have complained that everyone from their school teachers onwards have encouraged them to put their career first and never warned them that they would possibly have to give up the prospects of motherhood for this. For extremely intelligent women I sometimes despair at the naivety of this.

Only a short while ago I had lunch with such a lady. Anita had been on my register for quite a while. Her first introduction had seemed to go well but then after about a year it seemed to break down and other introductions after that had not been at all successful. She echoed all the sentiments I've said above. She had worked hard throughout the years to get to her present highly paid position in her career. Anita had bought herself a large house and had started to give herself more leisure time in that she was now only working a few days a week. Over the meal in a country pub she confided in me that if she could not find a mate then maybe she could have a baby before it was too late. She told me that the baby would need for nothing and that she would be able to spend more time at home than many other working mothers.

She put it to me that if I couldn't find her a husband could I find somebody who would father a child. "Well, no, I don't do that," I said. Her parting words were, "Please see what you can do."

When thrown down a challenge it is very difficult for me to ignore it. I thought about all the pitfalls this could lead me into if I ever approached a man on such an enterprise. I must admit I did contemplate for a few moments whether I could help as, at times, I do get men joining who desperately want to have a child. I thought of artificial insemination and two doting parents living in their own homes and not sharing each other's lives but sharing the life of their child. No, I couldn't get involved in this. Especially since in many cases men do want desperately to have a baby son simply to hand their farm onto. Sons don't always come first time or at all, and then they would want him to be brought up on the farm.

So I decided to trawl through the internet. I came up with several respectable clinics that provide help through artificial insemination by donor. In fact those in the USA would send everything in a kit by post! Initially you decided the type of man you would like to be the father of your child. You could print out the list - fair hair, dark hair, tall, academic, outdoor type, you name it they'd got it. You told them what you wanted and they reserved the semen for you. A kit would then be sent through for you to identify your fertile days. This was followed by another kit arriving on your most fertile days by special delivery containing the frozen semen specially ordered and packaged for you to thaw out and with which you would personally inseminate yourself.

I printed out all the pages and sent them to her saying I felt I had done what she had asked me to and supplied her with a father for her baby. She is thinking about it very seriously.

There are some high achieving women who go about finding a husband with the same efficiency that they conduct their jobs. Recently a lady of 42 wished to join who insisted that her introduction read both the Telegraph and Spectator. Not one or the other but had definitely to read both, play cricket and listen regularly to 'Sorry I Haven't a Clue.' He must also enjoy poetry and classical music, not one or the other, no give or take. He had, without any exception, to fulfil all those demands. I told her quite bluntly that I couldn't help.

Of course there has always been inequality of numbers in the different ages. There are always more young men seeking a partner than young women. So men in their twenties and early thirties are at a disadvantage. Apparently there are always more male babies born than girls and this filters through to the marriageable age groups. Throughout history men have been killed in wars and conflicts which have possibly then left an equal number of the sexes. Thankfully these wars do not happen now on the same scale. The numbers start to be balanced on my register at about thirty five years of age and stay that way until forty when quite rapidly more women come forward.

I have my own radical ideas about this inequality in the age groups searching for a partner. I often think the best solution to the problem would be to turn all our expectations of a mate completely upside down and get everyone to look at life, sex and marriage from a completely different view. If an older woman with her own home and financial independence finds herself alone either through widowhood or divorce would it not be advantageous to both if she were to seek out a much younger man of twenty five? This would provide much needed help, support and financial security for the younger man who would now not have to struggle too hard to get established.

By the time the husband was about fifty, one would assume that he would wish to have children and as the older lady would now be seventy five, she should welcome a new young wife to be accepted into the marriage. Any man of fifty would love to have a wife of perhaps twenty five who he could provide for financially by this time. Children born into this relationship would also give the very much older wife an interest and boost to her ageing life as a new 'grandmother.'

She would have had to be content that she experienced great things when she originally married her older man fifty years previously and produced his children when in her twenties and he provided her with all she needed. Then when he died and her children were grown up and left home she experienced for twenty plus years the joy of being with a much younger man, eventually to support him in his quest for a family when she was seventy five years old.

Yes, of course this notion is ridiculously simplistic. Men of twenty five do not fancy fifty year old women even though more and more women of fifty still look great. This would however solve the difficulties of so many unattached older women who will spend years alone and would solve the problem of many unattached younger men who also find it difficult to meet a marriage partner.

Other difficult aspects of finding introductions are for men who are particularly short or particularly thin. Maybe shortness is the worst. Most women like a man who is tall and certainly taller than they are. When a man of five feet, two inches applies to join I know his chances of success are reduced. Sometimes if I set up a meeting it works out well because his personality can be great and overcomes his shortness. I've found that short men very often have a fascinating personality. Possibly they have subconsciously developed something quite special to make them stand out.

I did have one man who joined the Bureau who I thought I would never be able to help.

Harry was a farmer aged forty three from Wiltshire and he asked me to drive down to see him. He said he did not go out much and wanted me to see him in his own environment. It was a small and beautifully kept livestock farm. When I met him I saw he was only about four foot, four inches in height and had a severely disfigured back. I felt I was facing a very big challenge. I suppose he had had that sort of test all his life and still faced the world with a smile and great hope. I knew I could not be pessimistic with him and talked about his future with optimism and confidence. But we also talked about the reality of his situation.

We walked around his farm, which was small and had been handed down to him from his parents. He was an only child and really did not have a lot of contact with other people except to sell his stock. His farm was immaculate. Not one blade of straw was out of place in the calf pens as I walked through his buildings. The alleyways were scrubbed clean and obviously washed down every day and the calves looked in superb condition.

He had adapted all his machinery to accommodate his height and, although old, it was all in pristine condition and sparkling clean. In fact everywhere looked as if it was endlessly washed with the concrete throughout his yard being spotlessly white. Everything seemed so organised and had a place; wellingtons had their own little covered house outside the back door and on the other side of the door were beautifully painted individual kennels for his sheepdogs. Not coming into contact with many people these dogs would be Harry's sole companions for many days. Their names were lovingly decorated on the kennels with painted flowers and birds interweaved throughout the decoration. I had never seen anything quite so ornate for a dog but it showed his artistic talent to the full.

The interior of the farmhouse was a duplicate of the yard and outside buildings. Lovingly decorated and tidy and clean. He showed me pictures of his parents who had died a few years ago and as I began to know him better his character shone through and I ceased to take any notice of his immediate physical appearance. This could happen in a dating situation with the right match. As he started to relax in my company more of his character came to the front. He then said that he wanted to show me something that he had never let anyone else see. He set in front of me handwritten poems that he had written over the course of time describing his loneliness, despair and sadness at how he looked. How painful it was to be as he was - the whole ironic and despairing tragedy of this normal man struggling to be recognised and treated as an ordinary person. I couldn't help but weep a few tears in recognition of how he had felt throughout his life.

I came away from his farm determined to do my utmost for him. In the course of time many women did reject him. Then, one day I had a women from Warwickshire join who was only four feet ten inches in height. On her registration form she had written down that her favourite pastime was writing poetry! I wondered, could it be that Gillian would accept an introduction to Harry?

I initially introduced Gillian to Harry in a very positive way, talking about his lifestyle and character and their mutual interest in writing. Then I brought in some facts about his appearance and asked her to think hard and not to dismiss the idea of meeting him immediately. She got back in touch and after much thought said she would go ahead. Because I wanted it to go so well I actually accompanied Gillian on their first meeting, which I had only ever done occasionally. I was there when they first met and sat between them talking to them both. As the date continued to go well I discreetly left them together. I can remember retreating to a sitting room in the small hotel. The venue had been carefully chosen as it was quiet but was also a place where they could walk in the grounds a little and sit privately.

To my utter delight they got on very well together. As we were coming home Gillian said that there had been definite moments when she had forgotten his height and the condition of his back and had begun to like him for himself. They spoke on the phone many times after this and then Gillian went down for her first visit to his farm.

It seemed in no time at all that I was told they were planning their wedding and within a very short time I'd had a wedding photo sent with a thank you letter. Then within the year I received another photo showing them with their new baby. I have to admit I was overcome with tears of pleasure at this wonderful ending.

Tall women, on the other hand, can be easier to match. I think it's because men equate tall with slim and they visualize a modern day version of Ursula Andress striding out of the sea with long flowing blond hair and a sexy, slim and tall figure to die for. I have also very seriously been asked by one Gloucestershire farmer to look through my register and come up with a duplicate of Princess Diana!

Other introductions needing special attention have been with those living in the Falklands Islands, in the South Atlantic. They are such very isolated islands just off the coast of Argentina, many thousands of miles from Great Britain. Their way of life seems to be more British than Great Britain and the main part of their economy is sheep farming. I suppose unmatched men on these islands naturally turn to the adverts in the British farming press to find their soul mates. When I first approach the subject of meeting a prospective match in the Falklands most women cannot entertain meeting a man living such a long way away.

When I wished to telephone a Bureau member who lived on an outlying farm on the Islands in the 1980s I needed to know the times that their generator would be on. This was because without the power the telephone would not work. I always used to communicate by phone then as it took so long for post to travel the oceans.

The first lady was duly asked to go down there for a holiday after she had got to know the man by letter. I felt it was all very exciting and couldn't wait for her to tell me how she found everything. She telephoned me after about four days on the Islands and described how, when she landed after an eighteen hour flight, she felt everyone was watching her. It was as if they knew why she was visiting. By the time she had been there three days the man she had flown down to see had asked her to marry him and she had accepted. She told me she realised she could love him and the life on the Islands and so, on the third day, an impromptu engagement party was held at one of the settlements for them both.

Her letter to me said, "I returned to the UK for just three weeks to say goodbye to my family and tidy up loose ends and flew back down to the Falklands. I wanted to get married here, as it will be my whole future life. After the wedding we moved out to the farm eleven miles away from our nearest neighbour."

They settled in the Falklands and had children very quickly but sadly, a few years ago, they parted and got divorced. She did not return home as she loves it out there and I understand from my latest bureau member who lives in the Falklands that she has married again.

My second client from the Falklands described himself as a quiet, good and caring man in his mid-thirties. Once again the proposal came very quickly after my lady client visited him and I do know they are still very happy after ten years of marriage.

The next lady to fly down there telephoned me a few days into the visit and said, " It's awful - I don't want to stay down here another day. I don't ever want to see another penguin as long as I live. There are no trees and the scenery is completely dull." So she promptly came home without success.

A third marriage came soon after this and they are still happily married. My one disappointment is a father and son, both farmers, from the islands for whom I have not been able to find successful introductions. One can totally understand the difficulties in finding marriage partners. There are only about three thousand permanent residents on the Islands so it is just like having to find a mate from the inhabitants of a large village.

Over the years men involved in farming from other parts of the world have registered with the Bureau, mostly from Canada, New Zealand and Australia. I also had a man from South Africa whose wife had died and left him with seven children. He was obviously very determined that someone special should come into his life rather quickly as he had put adverts in papers in Australia and New Zealand as well. I have to admit I could not find anybody who would consider taking on seven children and moving to Africa but he let me know that he eventually found 'his woman' in New Zealand.

As I was sitting in my office one day quietly going about my business a huge shadow came across the door. I'd heard a vehicle arrive but I thought it was for the farm. Standing there was a near duplicate of Crocodile Dundee, dressed in shorts, large sun hat and with the deepest Aussie accent. He was on my register and when I'd sent him a profile to consider he'd decided to hop on a plane and come straight over to see her! No announcement, he just arrived as he was, still dressed for bush life. The woman I had written to him about was amazingly versatile because when I telephoned her that afternoon and said he had turned up she immediately said he should drive down to her and she would book him into a hotel close by. Thank goodness she took him off my hands. I never knew what eventually happened but I do know that she went out to Australia for a while but she did not let me know if she came back or settled.

I was asked to fly to St. Lucia in the Caribbean for a week, flight and all expenses paid, to interview a lady who had a plantation on the island. She wanted to meet a Scotsman who would like to spend the winter in St. Lucia with her on her plantation and then they could spend the summer in Scotland. "You should really meet me," she said. "Come over and stay for a week."

I had a delightful young woman in her twenties visit my office. She was an industrious girl used to working directly with all animals and would have made a valuable contribution to any farm. She was a relief milker, lambed sheep throughout the spring and was pretty, honest and sincere. She came from a farming family but both her parents had died and the farm, being tenanted, had gone back to the landlord. She now rented a cottage. She was a pretty, kind girl, all that any man could wish for. The first farmer I introduced her to courted her for about a year then persuaded her, near lambing time, to give up her job and her cottage and move in with him and his parents. When their lambing was over and she had worked every day for the family without any wages, he promptly told her she was not needed any more. She was devastated, of course, as she then had no home or job. I asked her to come and stay with us as a guest at Mere Farm and she was told she would not be allowed to work, just to have a holiday for a while. I felt responsible that she had lost everything in her life. Eventually, when her old employer heard of her plight, he offered her old job back. She still has not got her cottage back and has had to take lodgings in her village.

I have been asked what has been the most unusual type of man or date. Well, the calculated approach comes to mind. A country bank manager who joined the Bureau told me that in the course of the evening when he was out with a date he would, at regular intervals, make an excuse to go to the gents to do his calculations. He always took three pens on every date, a black, a red and a green. There and then he would start marking down points for the lady he was with. The red would be for her bad points - danger I assume. The green would be for her good points - green for go? With the black pen he would add them all up. Only at the end of the evening when he had added them up would he decide if he wanted to see her again depending if the green outnumbered the red!

I have been asked what I think was the worst thing that has happened through an introduction. In my mind I remember the very sad circumstances of a client who had been introduced to a farmer. His photograph showed a broad, beefy, masculine man who was well educated. I introduced him to Elizabeth as they had the same cultural interests; music, theatre and concerts, their ages were right and they were not far apart geographically. All had gone so well and they planned to marry. Elizabeth had met his family and friends and felt very much a part of his life.

When she telephoned again I thought it was to tell me about her wedding. Well, it was to a certain extent, but she sounded very distressed.

"We did get married," she said. "In fact it was a lovely wedding service and we had our reception at the hotel where we had the marriage ceremony. We had also decided to stay there for the first two days of our honeymoon. After that we were departing on a cruise from Southampton. But our wedding night was not how I imagined it would be."

I held my breath - I had no idea what was coming.

"When all our guests had left and we eventually went to our room, I was totally bewildered and utterly speechless when my new husband came out of the bathroom wearing a pink flowery woman's frock. I stood transfixed in complete shock. He then proceeded to explain that he hoped I would understand his need to dress in this way and even lifted up his skirt to show me his frilly ladies silk underwear, which he explained he'd bought specially for our honeymoon night!"

I was speechless upon hearing all this. Whatever does one say? Especially when an indication came from her that I should have known about his fetish. I did feel so very sorry for her and started to say the words that you would in such a situation. How very awful this must have been. She had no idea.

Apparently she walked out of the hotel that night and would not talk to him at all in the days afterwards. Her solicitor had set the process rolling for an annulment of the marriage. I think this was the worst incident not because I am criticizing the man for his unusual preferences but that he had not got the decency or courage to tell his prospective wife and had gone into that marriage deceitfully and dishonestly.

Not all of my experiences are good and as well as coming across dishonesty I've seen how unsupported girls can be so badly treated.

I had a telephone call from a girl of twenty to ask if I could find her a husband. She said she had seen my advert in the Nursing Times and wondered if I could help as she had to get out of the dreadful situation she was in.

I have often found that nurses enjoyed connections with farming and the countryside so for many years have advertised in nursing magazines. Maria explained that she had been brought over from her country in the Caribbean to work for a couple in England. He was a solicitor and she was a nursing sister. They treated her very badly. They didn't pay her but beat her when they wished and she was not allowed to talk to anyone. I still said that, regretfully, I could not help.

As time went on she telephoned me again just really to chat and feel that she had someone to talk to. As the weeks progressed she came to a point where she said she would kill herself rather than stay in the life she had.

I told John and he said, "You'll have to do something about it."

With much thought I knew I could not leave her like this. Next time she telephoned I asked her if she would like me to come and fetch her from the house and bring her to my home. She was ecstatic and it was arranged that I would drive down the next day and just whisk her away. I arrived on the doorstep when the solicitor and his wife were at work. I had never met her before but she gratefully left the house with what she stood up in.

We drove home and after a few days with us she started to relax and not look completely like a terrified child. We wrote a letter to the family and said she was well and wanted to start a new life away from them. It was posted from Scotland so they had no idea where she was. Maria settled into life at Mere Farm well. She began to love my children and after a while we got Maria a job looking after an elderly lady on the south coast.

It all went very well in that she saved hard and learnt to drive and eventually bought herself a car. I would go and visit her about every six months and had such delight in letting Maria treat me to wonderful meals out and drive me about in her car.

The lady who she looked after adored her and taught her the ways of an English lady. Maria led a very happy life and when her employer died she left Maria all her beautiful antique furniture and quite a large legacy.

She had been going out with Thomas for about two years so they decided to purchase a twelve bedroom, residential home for the elderly. Maria would run it and Thomas would continue to run his business. The home they purchased is a beautiful large Georgian house tastefully furnished with Maria's antiques. She employs a cook and about five ladies and supervises the whole business brilliantly. I am spellbound when I visit her and see how she has progressed.

The lovely ending to this story is that recently she gave birth to a gorgeous baby daughter. I was asked to spend a few days with Maria and Thomas just after the birth. During that time they asked me to be the baby's honorary grandmother and hoped that she would always be able to call me grandma in the future.

15

Gather Ye Rosebuds

I started the Bureau in 1982 and never imagined it would continue to exist for such a long time. I envisaged closing it down once I started to have a family. However it's immediate success was so apparent that when the children did arrive I recognised the fact that I enjoyed the work, it seemed to be a much needed service and the business was flourishing.

The first anniversary came along and I was amazed that I had been working in this chosen field for a whole year, and that it was still going well. Each year after that, on the anniversaries, I would give a moment's thought to 'another year gone,' but usually I'd be so busy actually completing Bureau work that I didn't deliberate too long.

When an incredible five years had gone by I thought we should mark it with an actual celebration. So on that anniversary in 1987 Farmers

Weekly said they would like to do a piece to mark the five years and asked if they could interview me and several couples who had met through the Bureau.

The day started with a journalist from Farmers Weekly arriving. I took her to my office, as I do with clients who come for an interview, and settled her into one of my comfortable armchairs with coffee at her side. There was no preliminary chatting about the day ahead. She was obviously a professional and keen to go straight into the interview. Her first question was certainly to the point. She asked me why a bureau of this kind was needed for the country community.

I answered with precise and frank replies as I thought she would appreciate straight forward talking. I described the geographical isolation that many farming and country people accept as part of their normal existence, their irregular and long work hours and coupled with these two factors the lack of confidence and shyness that so easily develops in these circumstances. Not always, of course, and no doubt organisations such as Young Farmers Clubs are invaluable in helping a young person be more extrovert and confident.

I emphasised the point that a high percentage of the rural population have a quietness of character that is a definite hindrance when developing relationships with the opposite sex. In addition rural people have far less opportunity to mix than those living in larger towns or cities. I went on to describe women who have grown up in the countryside but have moved to urban areas for work. They too find it hard to meet someone who shares the same culture and background that they were brought up in. You don't meet many farmers teaching in inner city schools and of course all this can add up to difficulties in finding that special person.

We then moved into the farmhouse and as each coupled arrived they joined us in the sitting room. It is a long and narrow room with conservatory windows at one end and a good view over the garden and fields. Immediately you could see that the journalist was very interested in the couples assembled.

Giles and Angela sat on a settee together and described their wedding celebrated just the week before. It had been very quiet in the little country church in Angela's village. They had then spent a week in the

Lake District and had kindly returned a little early to be there that day. When asked about their lives they both declared they were in their fifties and had both been widowed quite early. Giles was a tall slim man with receding hair, a weathered thin face, but as straight as they come. He described himself as a 'dog and stick' farmer. "I first made sure Angela realised I was not landed gentry," he stressed.

Angela had been widowed several years previously but now worked as a farm secretary. She also did milk recording for local farmers. Short and petite with a lovely complexion and very quiet she described how she knew Giles was special the very first date they had.

Together they went on to talk about where they had been for their honeymoon and the life ahead of them. They had specific plans for it had been decided that Giles would retire and sell his farm. That would allow them to move into Angela's cottage situated in a beautiful little village. This would give both of them a comfortable life from then onwards. You could see the reporter had started to be a little spellbound by this older couple who had found what so many others half their age had not.

Then we approached Eric and Gillian as they sat drinking tea in two separate chairs. I told her about the lovely wedding that they had had. They had been married for a year and Eric described how he had proposed to Gillian at her farmhouse whilst helping to dry the dishes. He was a gamekeeper and his wife had died about five years previously. Gillian was farming the family farm. Gillian's husband had died several years previously and as well as a soul mate she needed a man who knew about country life but had not got a farm of his own. "That would have complicated things too much - we would not have known which farm to give up," said Gillian.

I recalled how difficult it can be to find a truly genuine man when you are a woman farming on your own. Now over the years I have found that so often it is not usually best to introduce a female farmer to a male farmer. So often they are torn between farms and I have seen relationships that could have worked otherwise completely fall apart due to neither being able to give up their farm. I continued to describe how men like gamekeepers and agricultural contractors often seem to be the best for women like Gillian as they are country men but do not have the complications of their own farms.

We all had lunch, and afterwards the journalist admitted that talking to my happy couples was enough to make the most cynical hack take a less jaundiced view of life. The article appeared in Farmers Weekly in the spring of 1987 and was called ' Mix 'n' Match.'

By 1992 the Bureau was ten years old and to celebrate I took a stand at the Royal Show. I had never done anything like this before and was quite apprehensive as I would be the only introduction agency there and I was not sure what the response would be. I really wanted to stand out and be different but on the other hand I could not afford a large and expensive area.

For my small exhibition at the Royal Show I decided to veer away from the clean cut lines of selling tractors or wine and I decided to have a romantic, flowers and hearts theme. The whole of the area was lined in a chintzy pink and cream material covered in huge pink roses. Explanations of the Bureau's work were mounted on pale green material backed boards which melted into the chintzy background. There was a patio and garden area at the back. This allowed a bit of privacy for people to sit with me. All in all I was very pleased with the romantic rural garden effect.

I thought lots of new people would become interested in the work of the Bureau, take a brochure home and consider getting in touch a few weeks later. This scenario worked to a certain extent but in fact the stand became the centre for many of the couples at the Royal Show who had met through me in previous years. Some brought their children to meet me. Other members of the family were introduced and all in all on the back patio it was a continuous great celebratory party for nearly a week. A great couple from East Anglia who were one of my first couples to marry brought their three children along to meet me. A newly engaged couple presented themselves along with a grandmother who was accompanying them. One couple told me about the birth of their twins, which they had not expected at all. Living on a very isolated farm she had not been to any ante-natal appointments. When the birth happened they had the surprise of their lives for out popped large and healthy twins.

Sadness came to the stand when I was told by one wife that her husband had developed an inoperable brain tumour.

I had some good fun on one of the days with the arrival of male twins from the Welsh borders. Great big well built fellows they were who were so funny in their everyday speech. Everything was a joke and their lives seemed totally full of humour but they wanted just one thing; to both find love and romance at the same time.

All in all it was a good week at the Royal, but not a lot of people joined the Bureau through my stand. I learnt why not afterwards. The big difficulty seemed to be that as I was always there people preferred not to come up and take a brochure. Apparently if I am there they feel I am going to pounce upon them and embarrass them there and then, maybe even with their friends by their side.

So I have found that people linger more if I am not around. Now when I occasionally have a stand at a little local agricultural show I go away and by doing this I get far more interest. I've been told by other stand holders that often the person picking the brochure up is being egged on in a jokey way by others, but really they do want a brochure and secretly are pleased they've got it and put it away to read quietly at home.

For the twentieth Anniversary I decided to invite twenty couples who had been successful though the Bureau to a celebratory lunch. They were couples that I had either never been able to meet personally but had got to know very well on the phone or couples who I'd met previously but had not seen for quite a while. I decided that I did not want the press involved on this occasion. I wanted to take pleasure in the day with my special guests and for them to thoroughly enjoy themselves as well. I had arranged that they would all arrive at Mere Farm from about 11 o'clock. The farmhouse was spruced up and the Bureau office had been redecorated. We even laid new turf down to make a small lawn and fresh flowers were cut and arranged. I bought a lovely new silky ice blue dress and my present secretaries and several who had worked for me in the past were invited to meet everyone and join in.

Guests started arriving. Some I had actually met but many had been just voices on the other end of the phone and it was wonderful to actually meet them at last after years of being very good friends. The sun shone as John and I greeted newly arrived couples outside the farmhouse front door. Others walked around the garden, a few, as we knew some farmers would, took it on themselves to walk around the farm and survey the stock - 'Can't they ever leave it alone?' one wife said. Two couples arrived who had not yet married and flashed engagement rings to everyone.

One of the couples was from the southwest. He was a dairy farmer from the Bristol area and said how he usually milked three times a day so he just would never have the time to go out and find a partner in life. By joining the Bureau he had met a lovely sweet natured young lady and they were planning their wedding soon.

As everyone arrived and couples were relaxed and talking freely my secretaries served champagne on the lawn. We all wore a yellow rose to indicate that we were 'staff'. From about one o'clock everyone departed to the local hotel that I had chosen as a retreat for the day. It was a perfect place in that it was only a ten minute drive towards Dove Dale and its renowned beautiful scenery. The hotel was extremely old, dating back to the sixteenth century and built of stone with tiny leaded mullion windows. The whole building was Tudor in design and small enough to close its doors that day to any other guests. Some of the couples had arranged to stay overnight so they could enjoy the day and evening without the worry of driving home.

As we all assembled we were greeted with romantic melodies from the pianist who had been drafted in specially. Sadly we were not able to accommodate children but Ben and Sarah accompanied us to the lunch and Sarah, now fifteen, handed round nibbles while Ben, seventeen, carried trays of drinks.

Ben and Sarah initially complained that they had got to join a party of such old fogies but Sarah did actually enjoy the dressing up. She was allowed to go with a friend and buy a new dress to wear. She choose the most clingy and provocative pink affair you could imagine. Of course it was foolish of me not to go with her which I would have done had I known what she was going to buy! However, I have to admit she looked gorgeous. Seventeen year old Ben had been bribed, with cash, into wearing a suit. It was the only way!

The lunch was presented with interesting romantic touches that the chef had taken great delight in inventing; heart shaped melon with ruby red raspberries were for starters followed by swans made out of pastry and filled with asparagus tips. The swans, so the chef told me later, represented lifelong love and devotion. This accompanied the main course, of heart shaped salmon. The inventiveness of the chef throughout was fascinating and caused much intrigue as to whatever would be presented next. Heart shaped individual cheesecake was offered with the puddings and he had even had the local chocolate manufacturer produce special heart shaped mints which were given in a presentation box to mark the day.

After lunch we had some speeches for, unknown to me, my secretaries had arranged for a few couples to say some lovely words. John read out letters received from two successful couples in the Falklands Islands, hoping everyone would have a great day. I cut a celebratory cake and we all joined in a champagne toast to couples everywhere who are together because of the Bureau. I sat back and looked on as everyone enjoyed themselves.

I watched a couple at the far end of the room laughing and joking with others and remembered the man who had sat in my office and cried because of the very difficult stutter he had. I suggested he write letters to his introduction but he was worried as he knew he did not write too well. So I helped him write his letters. All went so well and the next time he visited me he was with his new wife, several days into their honeymoon and he sat and cried again but now with tears of joy and happiness.

My mind brought me back to the happenings of that afternoon and I decided I should start to mingle with my guests. I was amused to see Ben was quite convinced that we did not realise he was dodging out of the room regularly to have a cigarette as he knew we would not have approved. He was growing up so fast. I was less amused when I saw Sarah making eyes at one of the younger waiters. Whatever did she think she was doing!

The day ended in the early evening with the couples promising to keep in touch with others they had met and me. We all had such a good time. John and I and the children returned home in a taxi. The children went straight into the farmhouse and, amazingly for once, did not turn on their loud music. I think they were both nicely mellow and about to drop as they'd readily participated in the free drink. John and I sat down on our patio. You know how you feel when you've had such a busy day. You just have to unwind a little. "I'm bloody knackered,"

John said. I laughed and without saying a word decided to savour the lovely day as I listened to the cows munching on their grass and enjoyed the strong floral summer smell that wafted through the air. After a while I became aware of another sound, quite hazy and repetitive - John was fast asleep and snoring. What a romantic end to the day!

The next morning I got up as usual and continued my normal routine of Bureau work, reading through forms, matching up others and writing letters. I felt in some ways it was a new start; I'd done the first twenty years and now I was beginning again and looking forward to all that was in front of me in the years to come. It felt good. My introduction agency had 'come of age;' it was now in it's twenty first year.

I allowed myself, today of all days, to think back. I thought of John and remembered back to the pouring rain and providence that obviously decided to put us together and felt very lucky that we had been able to enjoy such a happy marriage.

It has often been said to me that a man can have everything; a large farm, good health and wealth, but all that means nothing if he wants someone to share his life with and there is no one.

Most of us have no idea how difficult it can be when you live in a very isolated country location or suffer from debilitating shyness and a lack of confidence. But if only people could get out there and try meeting others and keep trying. If you don't find a lover, you might find a friend. Whatever, just keep trying and don't think that because you're using an introduction agency you need to hide the fact. So many people out there have found what they have been looking for. They didn't simply give up at the first hurdle and success did eventually come their way.

Physical compatibility is, of course, important. I am not in any way saying they must be beautiful, attractive or handsome, but there must be that little 'extra' compared to the thousands of people you meet in everyday life. I sometimes ask people how they felt when they stood close. Did they feel comfortable? Did they smell nice? Not a perfume deodorant smell but the right smell for them.

I do wonder if the new age of electronic communication is going to make a significant difference. It's certainly much easier to communicate at least on one level - that of talking and listening. But can you really have a satisfying relationship over the air waves? If you're mucking out or in the milking parlour and you get a vibrating feeling in your trouser pocket do you get a thrill of anticipation knowing that the girl you chatted to on the internet last night might be sending you a text message? How much better to hold her in your arms, look into her eyes and feel a responding hug.

As for the question of the part played by the Matchmaker in putting two people successfully together I cannot really decide, even after 20 years of listening, deliberating on problems, taking chances, experiencing failures and advising. Maybe all of this is a combination of experience and what started as an undefined inner instinct but which has now come to be a refined skill. I'd like to feel, of course, that that is so but I know that maybe that it is just a part of it and you also need other elements. It could be coincidence or fate or am I just acting as a go-between for the powers that be. Maybe some greater power which knows everyone's destiny is just using me to put the whole jigsaw together.

I received a call recently from a lady in her eighties who explained that I introduced her to her husband when she was seventy two. She described sixteen wonderfully happy years of married life.

"I am letting you know that he died several days ago at ninety-two but I wanted to thank you for the lovely years I had with this great old man."

As I put the phone down her simple words convinced me that I had chosen the best job in the world.

Useful Contact Addresses

National Federation of Young Farmers Clubs
Young Farmers meet every week throughout most areas of the country. Young people up until 26 years of age meet together and enjoy rural activities, interests, competitions and have lively social gatherings.

Telephone 02376 857200   www.nfyfc.org.uk

Rural Stress Helpline
Volunteers at the end of a telephone line to listen to or to try to help anyone living a rural life and experiencing problems. This is a free and highly confidential service.

Telephone 02475 412916   www.ruralnet.org.uk

Country Link
In most rural counties Country Link organise regular 'get together' social events

Telephone 02259 655928

Farm Women's Clubs
Monthly social clubs held in most counties for rural women

Telephone 0208 6524927   www.fyi.co.uk

Association of British Introduction Agencies
Contact them for a list of approved and registered introduction agencies throughout Great Britain. To request a list by post send a large SAE to ABIA, 1st Floor, 35 Market Street, Tamworth, Staffs.
www.abia.org.uk

Farmers and Country Bureau
An Introduction agency for country people looking for friendship leading to a lasting relationship or marriage. A 16 page brochure is available.
Mere Farm, Bakewell, Derbyshire DE45 1LX

Telephone 01629 636281 (24 hrs)   www.farmersandcountry.co.uk

Farming Books and Videos ltd.,

Offering a wide range of publications for the working
farmer, smallholder and country dweller.

You've Done What, My Lord?

By Rory Clark

When James Aden applies for the position of Deputy Land Agent at one
of the finest landed estates in England, he little realises what he has let
himself in for. Negotiating with royalty, tenant farmers, lost parrots, escaping
sheep and the imperious Lady leghorn all appear to be part of the job description.

You've Done What, My Lord? was Rory Clark's first novel and was loosely
based on his experiences serving as land agent at some of the grandest estates in Britain, including the Althorp Estate in Northamptonshire, childhood
home of Princess Diana. It is a glorious insight into the topsy-turvy world of the
land agent.

An English Country Manner

By Rory Clark

When tragic circumstances force James Aden to leave Scotland he
eventually finds a new job as the agent on Sir Charles Buckley's vast
Suffolk estate.

Once again he has to deal with an unusual list of problems. Rogue chimney
pots, unsavoury tenants and delinquent sheep are just some of his responsibili-
ties. If only he didn't have to spend so much time worrying about the farm
secretary, Gail, and her rollercoaster love life then surely things would run
more smoothly.

Farming Books and Videos ltd.,

The Spacious Days
By Michael F Twist

This account of growing up on an estate at Burnham in Buckinghamshire in the 1920s and '30s recalls an agriculture in which there was a large labour force, time to do a job well and time to talk, chaff and enjoy a bit of Shooting. It is the first part of this classic rural trilogy.

These are tales about real people and real places providing an insight into days long gone when a caring relationship and natural balance still existed between man and nature. Indeed, for the author, nature in the form of pet foxes, stoats, squirrels and badgers was an intimate part of home life.

From his earliest days Michael Twist knew he wanted to be an estate manager like his father. He revelled in his world of Hampshire Down sheep, Berkshire pigs and cattle. He chased poachers, controlled vermin and helped at hay time and harvest. Above all he grew up to have an abiding love of the countryside and its inhabitants.

Hallowed Acres
By Michael F Twist

Growing up on an agricultural estate at Burnham, South Buckinghamshire gave Michael Twist a great respect for the land and the countryside. Fields were talked of as if they were living entities and labourers had a feel for the land, born of countless hours walking behind a team of horses or hand hoeing root crops.

In tandem with The Spacious Days, this second volume of Michael Twist's reminiscences is full of humour in its depiction of the characters on the estate and the experiences of a young lad growing into manhood. It tells of the wildlife that abounded through out the country, of his friendship with a family of true Romany gypsies, of country pastimes and of agricultural shows and competitions.

The Glory Days
By Michael F Twist

The Glory Days recalls one of the great ages of farming and a time when farmers were truly appreciated, ironically the Second World War. Successive inter-war governments had failed to support farming effectively but now the country required a massive increase in production from impoverished land. When the author is invalided out of the army and appointed estate manager on the run-down Roundhill estate in the Vale of Aylesbury, he knows that he must succeed, not just because Colonel Devereux will sack him if he fails, but because the country needs people like him to provide the food that will help to sustain the war effort.

The challenges Michael faces include restructuring the labour force with the aid of Land Girls, building up a high yielding herd of Dairy Shorthorns, setting up the first AI centre and organising what became the largest grass drying unit in the country.

He also reminisces about the challenges of maintaining rural traditions such as hunting against a background of fifth columnists, doodlebugs and uncertain news from abroad.

Farming Books and Videos ltd.,

One Dog and His Man
By Marjorie Quarton

One Dog and His Man follows the adventures of Shep, canine hero, TV star, sheepdog trials champion and narrator of this humorous book charting his rise from humble beginnings in Coolcoffin, Ireland, where he is aided and often thwarted by his comical but lovable owner, 'The Boss.'

From pre-novice class commands such as 'Comein, Get out, lie down damn you, Get up you uselfess eejit, G'way outa that and G'home you devil' Shep eventually trains his boss to championship level encountering fun, tragedy, mayhem and love along the way.

Also published by Farming Books and Videos

Talking Sheepdogs Derek Scrimgeour	Best selling sheepdog training manual guiding the reader through early stages to championship level.
The Secret Life of Cows Rosamund Young	Fascinating study of bovine behaviour including observations on self-medication
Get it Right! Roy Goutté	Obedience training guide for rescue or re-homed farm dogs or for those wanting to compete.
An Introduction to Keeping Sheep Jane Upton and Dennis Soden	An essential guide for anyone wanting to keep sheep covering selection, housing and feeding

www.farmingbooksandvideos.com

PO Box 536
Preston
PR2 9ZY